TRL/MAC/4/017676/87   29/95

After a Fashion

After a Fashion

Stanley Middleton

Hutchinson
London   Melbourne   Auckland   Johannesburg

This edition first published in 1987 by Hutchinson Ltd., an imprint of
Century Hutchinson Ltd., Brookmount House, 62–65 Chandos Place,
London WC2N 4NW

Century Hutchinson Australia Pty Ltd.,
PO Box 496, 16–22 Church Street, Hawthorn, Victoria 3122, Australia

Century Hutchinson New Zealand Limited
PO Box 40–086, Glenfield, Auckland 10, New Zealand

Century Hutchinson South Africa Pty Ltd.,
PO Box 337, Bergvlei 2012 South Africa

ISBN: 0 09 168420 X

Printed and bound in Great Britain by
Anchor Brendon Ltd, Tiptree, Essex

British Library Cataloguing in Publication Data
Middleton, Stanley
    After a fashion.
    I. Title
    823'.914 (F)   PR6063.I25

ISBN 0 09 168360 2

For my wife and family and all in Ward F18, Q.M.C.,
Nottingham, who made possible the completion of this
novel

I'll set a bourn how far to be belov'd
Antony and Cleopatra

1

The older man pushed back a cuff to consult his wristwatch.

'I must be off, Joe,' he said.

'No hurry, is there?'

'Well.' He stood painfully, feeling at his hips, looking about for his stick. 'That's one of the incomprehensibles of my time of life. There's no great sense of rush from minute to minute, and yet longer stretches, weeks, months, years skid past.' Looking out of the window, he straightened his back. 'It hardly seems ten minutes since I was telling you time was up when I was invigilating your "S" paper.'

'Fourteen years.'

'It will be. You're getting to be an old gentleman, yourself.'

'Thirty-two next.'

Henry Smith, the retired schoolmaster, had bent again, screwed up his eyes to peer out of the window.

'You've got visitors.'

'Who's that?'

'Children.'

They moved into the hall where Joseph Harrington helped his former mentor into his raincoat.

'Don't leave it so long next time,' Harrington ordered.

'I shan't now know the quality of the cuisine.'

Smith clumped off, digging into the long back-garden path with his stick. The children, two boys, stood inside the gate as if caught out by the opening of the door and the emergence of the broad figure. They stood politely aside to let him pass, but he stopped to speak to them. It was too far away for Harrington to make sense of what was said, so he stood at the door of his conservatory, and waited.

September spread thickly green in the garden, without signs of autumn. The unmoving air, overcast sky and mildness

1

matched the still brightness of rudbeckia, Japanese anemones, dahlias, chrysanthemums, the plethora of yellow and red dots of fruit on the distant apple trees. Harrington noticed an out-of-season bloom, one of five, he counted, on a huge shrub rose.

The boys advanced towards him, the taller one step ahead.

Both were dressed alike, in sweat shirts and khaki shorts; both were brown as if they'd just returned from holiday. They did not walk fast; the path was long. They halted two yards short of the water butt where he stood.

'Hello.' Harrington greeted them; he did not know their faces.

Neither boy smiled.

'Excuse us,' the elder began. 'We wondered if we could have some of your windfall apples.'

'What for?'

'To eat.' The younger child, eagerly.

'They're mostly cookers, I'm afraid.'

'We like stewed apples, and apple pie,' the elder explained, a shade impatiently.

'Our mum makes it.'

'I see. What gave you the idea of coming in?' His back gate was usually locked.

'We could see the trees over the top of the hedge with all the apples on, and we knew there'd be some on the floor.'

'Ground,' he corrected.

'Ground. We pushed the gate open.'

He looked at the candid faces which were lifted for the next awkward question. He'd left the gate unlocked for Herbert Smith.

'We weren't scrumping,' the elder child volunteered.

'Nor even thinking of it?'

All three grinned, pleased with their knowledge of human wickedness.

'Have you got anything to carry them in?'

'No.' The younger boy.

'Wait there, then.'

When Harrington returned with a plastic bag the boys

seemed not to have moved. A murmur of talk ceased the moment he appeared.

'They're not ripe on the trees yet, and these that have dropped off have been attacked by codlin moth.' He showed them the black-brown wound with its blush of red skin. 'Your mother will have to cut the bad bits out, so pick big apples.'

'They don't poison you, do they?' the younger boy asked. The elder sniggered.

'I eat them.'

'But not raw?' The big boy, knowingly.

The bag filled, he ushered the two towards the gate, where they thanked him and set off, silently once the garden was closed to them. He locked up, examined his defences, a heavy fence on a stone wall backed by a hawthorn hedge, and made his way indoors.

His sitting room smelt of Smith's pipe so that he opened his windows. The old chap, he concluded, had enjoyed himself on this his first visit for lunch. They had met occasionally in the street, at the Literary Society, at concerts, but only in the last few weeks had talked at sufficient length or intimacy for Harrington to make an invitation. Smith had appeared grateful, in his brusque way. 'You don't have to do this, Harrington, y' know.' He still used the schoolmasterly surname.

'No, sir,' Harrington mocked. H. T. W. Smith, B.A., B.Sc. (Econ), now in his seventies, had been widowed eight months ago, bore the loss stoically, found his way awkwardly in the new world.

'You don't know what it's like, Joe.' He'd learnt the modern nomenclature only this afternoon during their first meal together. 'We'd been married nearly forty-seven years. I still sit there and expect to hear the back door bang as she comes in from her shopping. And I expect I shall to the end of my life. Habit dies hard if bodies don't.'

The schoolmaster had fiddled with pipe and tobacco, blowing smoke, groaning as he writhed in his chair to get rid of a spent match.

'It's remarkable. Nothing's changed except what I might

3

call the essence of life. You meet the same old women in the street, the newspapers are full of the same crises, but she's gone, done, her days over.'

They had no children, Harrington recalled, and Smith's wife, thin as her husband was broad, had scuttled about her nervous ways, intent on husband, home and, some way behind, the Anglican church.

'It happens more to women than men.' Smith, enlightening.

'Are they better able to cope?' the pupil asked.

'At everything. That's what I've found. I wonder why I was the one left.'

'You don't want to die.' Harrington would not let the old man off lightly.

'And I don't much want to live, I can tell you that.'

Smith went on to boast that he could cook, and sew, and look after himself, but that it hardly seemed worth the effort; and yet he blew his mouthfuls of smoke, and stretched his legs, and held up his port to the light, and once nodded off, after a sharp exchange on the listener's attitude to *Hamlet*. Smith had taught history at school, but had read a great deal, and had felt it his business constantly to test his wits against bright boys, and in their specialities.

Smith had been unusual in that without disguising his attitudes or edging away from his beliefs, he'd listened to his pupils. 'You can talk to Smudger,' the sixth form had decided. He might be old, for all they knew still mentally reliving his war exploits, but he'd time for them, and not overmuch condescension. They could expect argument from him, irony, humour, but he treated them as worth hearing. It was said he despised the headmaster, conducted a vigorous war against both deputy heads and the administrative assistant, though the boys never heard one syllable of this from him; he taught with thorough strength, gave his free time and stumped about the corridors in his tweed suit with his pepper-and-salt hair, a power in the land at least amongst the students because he was not afraid to know something about them.

But when Joseph Harrington returned to Beechnall three

4

years back and had run up against his former master, retired to his home town, hair now white as wool, the old man recognized him at once but appeared to know nothing about his recent life. Vigorous as ever, opinions at the ready, Smith did not realize that Harrington had been married, that his wife had walked out on him and that was the reason his former pupil lived alone in his present large house, formerly his father's. Either people had not talked, or Smith had not listened. It was puzzling.

Harrington's wife had been known to everybody, a celebrity, a television actress. They had met when he was in his first year as a junior lecturer in literature at University College, London, and she was, in her own words, wasting her time in a West End musical. She could sing in tune, attractively, could be coached into dance steps, but wanted to do neither; she had just made spectacular television appearances as Juliet and Rosalind and was at that time preparing for Ophelia in the same series and for St Joan on the other network. Joe Harrington had been flattered by her attention, then knocked flat when he realized that Paulina Street, three years his senior, wanted to marry him. He did as he was told; wedding pictures were splashed over popular and serious papers alike. They honeymooned briefly in Italy and then returned, she to a Coward revival and fame or notoriety as a young, determined, scatty television housewife, while he rapidly completed the book based on his Ph.D.

Paulina had moved into his flat, no more commodious or convenient than hers, but her movables were fewer than his. She'd had the place redecorated while they were abroad, and they lived happily, madly, bumping into each other, he steadily, she in racketing bursts of energy on this stage or that studio. Three years later, after he had applied for a lectureship at the university in his native city, she had announced that she was about to divorce him. This had nothing to do with his move, for she had known he would have to leave U.C.L. She had fallen in love with a financial tycoon, a peer, she informed him without histrionics, and that was the bitter end.

5

Again he was floored.

He had suspected nothing; Paulina's irregular schedules had made easy the concealment of adultery. Up to the time of her announcement she had been, as always, warmly loving, playful, affectionate, able to sit down with him seriously to discuss her roles, intelligent, distantly interested in his application for university posts, fiery in bed when not too tired, the clever and talented woman he had married against his own expectations two years before.

He did not contest the divorce, though it featured in the papers, as did Paulina's second marriage. Battered out of his wits, he had crept back 'home' to this house, on the outskirts of the city, and become nobody.

Smith appeared to have heard, read, understood nothing of this.

Or tactfully kept his mouth shut. Or refused to raise a subject that revived his own tearing grief.

Harrington dawdled along the path, making occasional forays to pick up apples, which he arranged in neat groups. He threw one reject towards the compost heap, but it struck a low branch and ricocheted into the cabbage patch.

Whistling tunelessly and without reason, he decided he would spend the rest of the afternoon outside. He'd weed; a parcel of bulbs had arrived which could go in; he'd begin, even in this floriferous late summer, some of the changes he'd decided on.

The garden, and his work, had saved him. His six academically successful years at Cambridge had been desperate and lonely, but he had come to terms with parcelling out his time, by making meals or by supervisions given or taken, adding variation to the long hours of study. In London he'd begun, as he expected, in the same way, rewriting drafts of his thesis, preparing lectures, teaching; his life seemed marginally more pleasant, for his colleagues were hospitable, but his work occupied him. Only when he met Paulina Street, at a party given by a distinguished senior member of his department, did he learn, not without misgiving, to begin to break these habits. After the marriage, arranged and carried out within a few weeks of the first meeting, his life had been relaxed, warmer, full of the anticipation of the unexpected. Paulina insisted he throw away his pyjamas. He did so with joy, though squinting about for catastrophe.

Once Paulina had deserted him he returned as best he could to work, but now pain hindered. He remembered those nights in Cambridge, after early informal dinner, when he'd returned to his hot room and had sat fighting his books, dredging up brilliance, making his mark, knowing in spite of voices and footsteps on the corridors, shouting knots of people down there in the street, nobody would tap at his door. Those hours, anguishing at the time, now seemed pleasurable; profitable, prolific, a scholarly idyll.

Harrington did not give up. Since his arrival in Beechnall he had published his large, well-reviewed book on the pre-Romantics, placed articles regularly in learned journals where he had also done some just but appreciative reviewing, and had gone out of his way to complete a commission, a small book for 'A' level or first year university students on the poetry of Robert Frost. His publishers were now suggesting that he turned out a similar piece on Wallace Stevens. His career developed as it should; he did more, achieved more than his colleagues, and yet he was a nobody to himself, a stick, a scarecrow, a lay figure. By thirty he had lived his life.

He found himself as now standing on his garden path in a gloomy paralysis, not remembering, pondering or planning, merely quite still in numbness. From time to time bouts of violent grief attacked him, physically disabling him, leaving him incapable of reading or using pen or rake, but these lasted for short periods only, and he had devised methods of recovery.

Foolishly, a week ago, he had looked at the first of Paulina's new series on B B C 1. Here she played Phyllida Squires, the clever, sharp-tongued housewife who lacked common sense, who needed to be rescued by her husband from situations into which her donnish ferocity had tipped her. Feminists had complained at length in the quality papers, but the first two series had been remarkably popular, chiefly, it was

7

claimed, because women liked to hear a woman saying incisively what they could never quite put together, and because Mrs Squires was clearly incorrigible and would one week, before too long, lay all opposition flat. Harrington had disliked the first programmes when they were being screened in the last real weeks of his marriage; not on the grounds that its basis was too light weight for continued interest, nor because the script lacked wit – it did not – but because it could not offer sufficient scope for Paulina's talents as an actress. It coined her a great deal of money, made her face nationally known, even treasured, but was accomplished, as well she recognized, without much effort on her part. She had become famous without trying, with no sweat.

Harrington had turned on the programme, after a day's intermittent distress and self-argument. Phyllida Squires, beautiful and beautifully dressed, tore strips off the objections raised by a brace of cowboys who had come to repair her roof. She slapped them down with gusto, and one could guess that before twenty minutes had passed she'd be staring up at a slateless skeleton of beams and laths. Joe watched for five or six minutes, then staggered across the room to switch off. It was as if someone had landed a heavy blow on his solar plexus, winding him, knocking all humanity out of him. The sight of Paulina, and this role of clueless, beautiful shrew differed utterly from her ordinary presence, had beaten him down. He had dropped into his chair, trembling. That evening he had been unable to complete the small amount of not very exacting reading he had set for himself. He drank four cups of instant coffee, and shuddered at his vulnerability. By the next day, he was, he thought, himself.

Now on his garden path, on a Saturday afternoon, he tossed up an apple spinning in his right hand. He decided to change into gardening clothes; the casual things he wore, sports jacket, sharply creased trousers, check shirt and monochrome tie he had donned as suitable to H. T. W. Smith's social expectations. Harrington grinned, unable to discover why it had been important to impress this old schoolmaster. He bowled an off break down the path and his apple exploded.

From the distance he heard music and then a metallic voice from the public address system of a factory sports ground. Briskly approaching, he kicked the largest piece of apple on to the soil, went indoors.

Not a leaf moved.

2

At four o'clock on the third of October Joseph Harrington
pushed in home, snatched off his jacket and put on the kettle.
Tuesday had proved, as always, hard work. He had delivered
a lecture on Blake, and had taken a seminar, ten pupils, on
Chatterton in the morning, and in the afternoon had supervised three M.Litt. students on their research and its progress
during the summer holiday. He had been back at the university in his office or the library five days a week since the
beginning of September, but the opening lecture of the term,
even though he had delivered it twice before, invariably
depressed him, as did his interviews with the research
students who appeared awkward, impolite, unapologetic for
having wasted, in his eyes, or misused the vacation. Now he
whistled and prepared for an hour's leisure with the newspaper and tea pot before he set about his evening's work. He
had taken his main meal of the day at the university, listening
to the distant buzz about Venice or the Dordogne or the
surprise at appointments and applications as he sat facing
his professor, a rubicund bachelor in his sixties who seemed
interested nowadays in nothing except the eccentric behaviour
or notions of his fellow senior academics.

Today Professor Wainwright claimed he had just read the
lengthy examination of Cowper's language which had cost
Harrington painful weeks of thinking as well as some
computer-programming two years before.

'It's very good,' he pronounced, 'in its way. Very good
indeed. That is if I understand it. I ought, of course, to have
spent more time on it, but you know how it is.' The article
had been out for at least six months. 'You young men are too
mathematical – or is it philosophical? – for me.'

10

'How's that, Walter?' a disappointed senior lecturer had inquired, shovelling in a juicy forkful of mashed potato.

'I'm not sure that such treatment is requisite to a person like Cowper.'

'He uses language, doesn't he?'

'And language is a mystery. I know, I know. Pass me the salt, please.' A newly appointed lecturer complied. The professor smiled. 'Ah,' he said, gently rebuking, 'it has arrived, in spite of all complication. Still, I must compliment you, Joe, on your assiduity.'

'And intelligence?' The enemy at work. Satan Morris, the senior lecturer.

'You know, Harold, that I am incapable of any assessment of that.' The prof. salted his pale pommes frites. 'But Joe, at least, is occupying his time usefully before he attains a position where others will occupy it for him.'

'I wonder why one should be highly regarded for using one's wits on Blake or Joyce or Eliot, and not on Cowper. Or Hardy for that matter?' The senior lecturer's bile would extend itself on such queries for one week into term, before dying into lethargy.

'I am not good at riddles.' The professor waited to pounce, but nobody budged. 'Or anything else, eh, Harold?'

'You said that, Walter.' Everyone else on Christian name terms except that Morris called Wainwright 'Paul'.

' "What oft was thought. . . ." ' The head of the department eyed his plate dreamily. He'd spend two or three days this week with his underlings at the luncheon table, before he moved for the rest of the term into the company of the registrar, the dean of sciences, the professor of engineering, all exalted and influential. 'Has your book been reviewed yet in the *T.L.S*?' he asked the senior lecturer, knowing the ferocity of the attack there, with its large count of alleged elementary errors committed and the final accusation of a pretentious and misplaced conception. 'I must have missed it.' The professor had been earning money on the West Coast of America. He next bullied a lady lecturer about a book on Spenser she had been about to publish for the past five years, inquired about the failing marriage of a young Marxist he disliked, then fell into heavy silence, refusing to answer any question directed at him until his plate was empty, and his enemies' cups full and running over. He had walked out of the dining room with Harrington.

'The trouble with my department is self-satisfaction.' He sniffed. 'You are one of our few exceptions.'

Harrington had felt uncomfortable; praise often preluded an order to carry out some task he found unpleasant or was incapable of doing properly. The professor sidled off to juggle with someone else's future.

The subordinate felt uncomfortable in Wainwright's presence. The man had been clever, written a brilliant doctorate on medieval literature, which had been expanded into a book still highly regarded thirty years on, and then had settled into doing next to nothing. Neither idle nor malicious, he gave the appearance of both. He had published selections of Gower, Hoccleve and Dunbar; in the last ten years had produced school editions of Chaucer's 'Prologue' and the 'Knight's Tale' that were models of clarity and accuracy, but he never exerted himself mentally. He chased Helen Southwell about Spenser because he thought his chaff would help her finish the book; he had no idea of her difficulties, her doubts, scruples, delicate qualifications, her fine discrimination. There was no intention to hurt, merely to spur. He clashed with Harold Morris, the senior lecturer, out of a mischievous sense of duty, but to Harrington the old man represented unprofitability; these exchanges had more of squabbles in the infant playground than of wit-combat.

His kettle boiled; he lobbed teabags into the pot.

The front doorbell pealed.

Harrington coated the pot with a cosy, and made out into the hall. Somebody trying to sell him something. Or talk about eternal life or C.N.D. or double glazing.

A neat, youngish woman, dressed in a buff raincoat, with fair hair upthrust into a bun stood two yards back from the step. He looked at her without speaking, and for a moment she too was silent.

'Do you live here?' she asked awkwardly.

'Yeah.'

'I've tried, oh, three times in the last month to get hold of you, but you're never in.'

He did not answer the sentence, which made no sense to him.

'My name is Anne Selby.' Further pause. 'My sons came in and begged apples from you. I wanted to thank you.'

'That's all right.'

'I didn't think so. I wasn't pleased with them.'

'But you used the apples?'

She blushed to the roots of her hair.

'They had no right.' Mrs Selby seemed bemused by his question.

'Will you come in?'

'I don't want to waste your time.'

He explained the recreational nature of his next half-hour, so that she followed him into the kitchen where she unbuttoned her mackintosh. Undecided between cups or mugs, he eschewed formality. She examined the picture of Charles and Diana on hers with ironical interest.

'I was a bit cross with them,' she began.

'It showed initiative on their part.'

'And embarrassed their mother.'

He felt momentarily pleased with her company, kept quiet about it.

'That's why I was so determined to get hold of you in person and apologise, rather than phone.'

'I approve,' he said.

'Of what? Them? Me? My apology?' She giggled.

'The lot.'

They laughed together, made an attempt to sip their scalding tea. Anne spoke about her sons, George aged nine, William six, and their empirical approach to life. 'They act as I never would, even now.' Her husband, Anthony Selby, worked in the county library, was keen on computers, had a word processor at home, and was using it to write the life of his ancestor, Timothy Voisin Selby.

13

'I've never heard of him.'

'There's no reason why you should. He made a fortune in Canada, with a chain of shops, retired at fifty and took up religion.'

'Out there.'

'Out there.' She repeated his phrase as if its use had put him in the wrong, but immediately she reverted to family affairs. In return he explained what he did for a living.

'If I'd have known that, I wouldn't have dared to come,' she said, but she looked him over seriously, as if his casual clothes fell short of her image of a don. He spent a few moments on his interests; she interrupted, almost rudely, some sentences on Wallace Stevens to ask if he lived here alone.

'Yes.' He made the word grim.

'You're not married?'

'Divorced.'

'Oh, I see.'

He felt uncomfortable, even angry, as if she'd patronised him, but he offered her more tea. She refused and, slipping down from her stool, fastened up her coat. The breasts under the blouse were briefly beautiful. He had admired her ankles from first glance.

'Would you like some more apples? Windfalls?'

'If it's no trouble.'

'There are plenty. This weekend I shall have to see if those on the tree are ready.'

'This weekend I shall take the boys to Goose Fair.'

'Is that good or bad?'

She shrugged, and after he had rummaged for a plastic container, he motioned her out on to the patio. Unembarrassed, she helped him pick up the fruit.

'This is a lovely garden,' she volunteered. She had turned round as they sauntered back towards the house.

'Are you interested in gardening?'

'No. I help. Tony's not very keen, either. Fortunately we haven't got much, and that's mainly grass. And roses.'

'Privet hedges?'

14

'Yes.' She looked guilty.

Anne did not pause in the house, stepped straight for the front door, and thanking him still made speed along the path. Pouring himself a second drink, he looked at her abandoned stool and mug. Why was it so important to her that she had made three journeys to thank him for a few pence worth of apples? Where were her boys this afternoon? They'd be out of school. He had not asked these questions. This pale, sturdy woman had blood red fingernails, wore perfume. Interested, he put her from his mind and prepared to work.

He opened a letter by second post from his publishers in reply to his complaint that his Wallace Stevens book would take him too long. His editor sounded relieved, and offered in its place an equivalent primer on Yeats, or perhaps T. S. Eliot. It was necessary, in spite of all the extant books, Julian Festing pontificated; it need not be hack work and it would sell in good numbers. Harrington felt unreasonably pleased; Wainwright had lumbered him with some lectures on Eliot ('Your books on Stevens and Frost make you our first-choice contemporary expert now') and the coincidence seemed propitious. A quarter of an hour ago he had been trying to explain to Anne Selby what he thought about Stevens; now he need think no longer. Elation became disappointment. Ducking from difficulty meant the end of self-respect. He moved upstairs to his study to lose himself.

A week later he found a note through his door inviting him to lunch with the Selby family on Saturday. He immediately posted a letter of acceptance. On the morning of his visit, he had already packed a box of his best apples and chosen a bottle of wine as presents. He was setting off for his weekly drive to Sainsbury's when the postman, a new hand at the job and late, handed him an envelope, addressed in Paulina's hand.

Shaken, he unlocked his door to sit and read this.

The large envelope, the thick, headed paper seemed too good to spoil with writing, especially with a style as large and twiggy as his ex-wife's. Though the message took up two sides, it did not occupy much of his time. Paulina asked if it were possible for them to meet, since she would like to talk over a part she had been offered. She hoped he was well. His. Paulina.

Harrington trembled.

Since the divorce, loathed on his part, he had heard nothing of her.

The settlement of their financial affairs had not been satisfactory as far as his share was concerned. Paulina's solicitor had outgunned his, and though Harrington felt bitter, he knew he had tied his lawyer's hands by showing no interest in the fight against his rich ex-wife. 'I want it over. Get something for the flat, and half the contents, and that will do.' His man had argued; Harrington had shut his mouth with, 'I am not interested. Just do as I say. I'm not poor.' He had been numb, sick with the speed of her announcement, her certitude of decision, her ability to dismiss him and begin her new life. She had been equally hard, uncharitable, nastily predatory through her solicitor in the court.

He had not expected to hear from her again. Fiddling the paper from its casing he reread the note. It had not changed. The message was dashed off; she'd not sat long over that. Puzzled he placed it in the brass rack where he kept bills in the kitchen. The two had often discussed her theatrical roles together, but as far as he remembered he had never changed her mind for her. She listened to him; he often told her things she did not know, but that was all. Rarely satisfied with what she was offered, she compromised if the money were large enough. Her ambition for herself was towering, but she needed to live, and comfortably. Now as Lady Benson such financial considerations, except as psychologically based, were not important, he guessed, though he had not noticed any change in her acceptance of trivial parts during these last three years.

Paulina was in no need of his guidance about the theatre.

Perhaps she was curious, wanting to know how he muddled along. Perhaps even guilty, willing to make some reparation. That too was unlikely. What had wounded him most cruelly was her inhuman certainty. Our marriage is over. I have met

16

a more interesting man than you. Stop. Get out of my way. Stop. You can surely understand what I'm saying, can't you, and can see it makes sense?

Their warmth of life, laughter, comfort, their slow Sundays in bed or the car, or periods of absence, or exhaustion, their ecstasies of reunion were erased. He was a mere succubus, attached to her by a legal contract, and nothing else. Break that and forget, because she had forgotten already.

He trailed round the supermarket unable to concentrate on his shopping list; his wire-trolley wandered. Meticulously he retraced his footsteps, ticking off items. Why should he bother to reply to her? He composed small answers: 'Dear Lady Benson, The fee for a half-hour consultation is thirty guineas payable in advance. Perhaps you would telephone between four and five on Tuesday or Thursday for an appointment. Yours sincerely, J. J. Harrington.' Streaks of anger flashed: 'How the hell have you the bloody nerve to write to me?' or 'My interest in your theatrical career is minimal, and in that case no purpose would be served. . . .' He completed his shopping.

By the time he set off for the Selby household, he had come to terms with Paulina's demand, was enjoying the possibilities of reply, even admitting that he could bring himself to meet his former wife.

The Selby family occupied a small, detached house built within the last five years. The gardens were open-plan, the next street very close. 'You can see,' Anne Selby pointed out, 'our need for net curtains.' The boys tore about on lawns and in the crescent; new trees grew solitarily in every plot; cars were parked on drives or fronts. The district gave an impression of rawness, of young people on the move, to larger houses or to different cities and promotion. The elderly couple vigorously at work on the Ford Cortina opposite seemed out of place.

Anthony Selby, tall, handsome, with a cleft chin and polished spectacles began to talk about computers once his wife had gone out into the kitchen. Here was an enthusiast, full of schemes, uncomfortably aware that his boss, the director of leisure services, approved of the new technology without having any notion of how it could be used. Selby was launched into the details of his latest programme, which would lift art history from its haphazard bits and pieces into a small handleable empire; the man spoke well, kept Harrington occupied. Joe indicated his own corner of interest. Selby made useful suggestions.

Anne instructed her husband to get the boys inside and scrubbed for the table. He nodded a smiling by-your-leave to his guest, and was seen seconds later in the street shooing his captured sons pell-mell indoors. Jollity from the scullery spoke the popularity of father or food.

All sat down to eat heartily; there were no saucy plates. The boys argued between mouthfuls about a football match played earlier in the morning at the school. They talked freely, but listened politely as their father interrupted with an irrelevance about a meeting he'd had with the manager of the local first division team at an exhibition of computers. It must have been recently for the children had not heard the tale before; they listened wide-eyed; their dad had spoken to God.

The younger boy knocked over a glass of orange; without fuss his mother mopped the cloth, refilled the righted glass while father, after one jovial comment, continued with the previous topic. The males did their best not to exclude Harrington; their mother smiled, and dished out large helpings. When the meal was over, the boys shot away; the grown-ups drank coffee, still at the table. Harrington helped Anne to wash the dishes.

'I hope you don't mind that we have to throw you out soon. Did Tony make that clear?'

He had not; Harrington pulled faces to prove he had.

'This is the day for visiting grandfather.'

'Your father, or your husband's?' Did it matter?

'Mine.'

'Do they like that?'

'Not really. But there's a good football ground nearby and they all go off to see the game. If it weren't for that I don't think I'd send them. As it is, it's only about once a month.'

18

He did not reply, and she, disappointed apparently, continued.

'My father can't stand too much noise.'

'Is he old?'

'Not really. Sixty-six. But he lives on his own now.'

'Widower?'

'No. My mother's still alive. She lives in Dorking. They divorced, and she married again. I don't blame her. He took some living with.'

Harrington was amazed at this early frankness, then thought it suggested distance between them; she could talk thus to a stranger who lacked real concern. When Tony reappeared, she packed a basket with iced buns for tea, inspected the faces of the collected boys.

'Would you like to come with us?' Tony asked Harrington. 'We learn a lot about life from the footballers.'

'That fat goalkeeper,' said the older child.

'Especially.' Their father. They laughed.

Harrington refused, with a specious excuse. He said he hoped they'd visit him one day.

'You can't cater for all of us,' Anne demurred.

'No, but I'd try.'

When he arrived home, he saw Paulina's letter in pride of place on the mantelshelf. The hour or so with the Selby family had not exactly driven it from his mind: the note had stained his mood, not changed it.

He decided against replying immediately, though he knew what he would say: he was willing if she saw any advantage in the meeting. She was to suggest dates and venues. He was hers sincerely.

3

Harrington did not post his letter until midweek, deliberately delaying. Within two days Paulina had replied, suggesting that she and Edmond, her husband, would visit him at half past two on Wednesday next. He was to do nothing about food, for they'd have lunch on the journey, and would not stay to dinner as Edmond had a speaking engagement that evening in Newark. She'd be most grateful if he could try to clear his afternoon for them, because otherwise it would be some time before she could conveniently come up again. Would he please confirm that Wednesday suited?

The letter irritated him, in that this time it was typed. He, moreover, guessed that she had decided on dropping in once she had made the arrangement to accompany her husband to his dinner in Newark. He doubted whether she needed advice about a script; this was a tour of inspection, mooted in mischief.

He sent his acceptance, 'Wednesday fine', on a postcard of views of the city. The garish sky, the buildings reduced to thumbnail size, pleased him, insulted her, gave the proper riposte to her heavy paper, parchment-thick envelopes.

On the day of the visit he lingered over his lunch at the university and then found himself driving home at speed. He had tidied the house, telling himself that this was unnecessary, but primly moving furniture or bric-à-brac, he had approved the effect. The sun emerged, after a dull morning, to burnish his surfaces.

It was nearer three than the arranged two-thirty when the Bensons arrived.

Paulina rushed at him, snatched a kiss at his cheek, patted his forearms, looking as nervous as he felt. Edmond Benson, Lord Benson of Louth, was tall, grey-suited and haired, with

20

an attractive wrinkle or two, but slim and fit enough for a sharp game of squash. He shook hands solemnly, said he was glad.

From the window of the dining room which overlooked the length of back garden Paulina put on a small performance.

'It's quite rural,' she said. 'I'd no idea. An estate.'

He offered them tea or coffee; again she surprised him by choosing the former. Paulina recovered form by asking for lemon in hers. Harrington made the effort; he could not remember her drinking much besides black coffee. They drank seated round the table, Lord Benson even accepting a chocolate biscuit. Talk flowed more easily than Harrington had expected; Benson, who knew the city well, made tactful, interesting conversational forays, drawing polite replies from his host. Paulina intervened with fidgety, disconnected sentences.

Benson finished his tea, looked at his watch, said he had a call to make, on a former chief clerk, and this would take perhaps an hour. With permission he'd leave his wife here, and collect her at four-thirty. Paulina gabbled explanations about her husband's need to arrive early, settle his nerves, practise his speech before the dinner. Benson acquiesced with a repeated 'no', a carved smile, a flutter of the right hand.

When Harrington had let the man out, Paulina had not accompanied them to the door, he returned to find his ex-wife again at the window.

'Well,' she asked, wheeling, 'and how are you?' His noncommittal replies did not appear to disconcert her, and after refusing more tea, she came with *élan* to sit opposite him. Again he saw the fine dark eyes, high cheekbones, the intelligent set of the shoulders. She made her body think and talk. The clothes were casual, even unsuitable; jeans and an open necked blouse, with a thin silver chain just visible. Her earrings flashed, small and circular; her eyebrows were thinned to a curve. Harrington felt pain at her physical presence, relived distress but found it bearable.

'I expect,' she said flatly enough, 'you wonder why I'm here.' She featured a favourite aunt with an awkward child.

'I wanted to see how things were with you. I'm still interested, you know.'

He answered that he had plenty to keep him busy.

'You're not thinking about remarrying?' Paulina made no bones of it.

'No.'

He did not observe her reaction, made her waste time and talent. Since his arrival here he had burned through two affairs, ferociously short, one with the wife of a colleague, the other with a bright research student. Both women, he guessed, had been relieved when they had called it a day. Unsatisfactory was the word he chose for himself.

'You should,' she remarked, but he kept silent. As she crossed and uncrossed her legs, he remembered the movement poignantly, knew hurt again. 'I want to ask you about myself.' She waited now, forcing a reply out of him.

'Yes?'

'Shall I give it up? My career?'

'And do what?'

He guessed she did not wish to discuss this, had raised it by default, unseriously.

'Be Edmond's wife.'

'Is that a full-time occupation?'

'Easily. He's an estate in Hampshire, as well as a London house.'

'And you'd have children?'

'I don't know about that. Edmond has two sons by his first marriage.' Harrington already knew; he'd consulted *Who's Who*.

'Don't you have any say in it?'

'Of course.'

Now he waited; certain of where to go next, but uncertain of himself.

'You've given the answer,' he said in the end. 'If you don't have children you may as well stay in the theatre.'

Paulina straightened her back.

'You surprise me. So looking after my husband, and our

22

homes, doesn't count for anything. Is that what you're telling me?' Why this hysteria?

'What does he do that's so special?'

'His directorships involve a fair amount of travel and entertainment. With fringe political activities. And though he's energetic the day may not be far off when he wants to ease himself out of these commitments, retire, spend more time at home, spoil himself.'

'Curious expression.'

'What is? What are you talking about, Joe?'

' "Spoil himself." Isn't that about right?'

She looked at him, a gimlet of hate in each eye.

'You wouldn't say that if you knew him.'

Harrington did not answer, determined to act awkwardly. Her presence, the magnificent physicality, rocked the room, bruising him. He scowled, kept his trap warily shut.

'Why are you considering it now?' he asked reasonably, once he managed to speak again. 'Have you had some offer that might tie you down? Or is your husband not well? Why is it important to make your mind up now?'

'It isn't.'

'What are you doing here, then?'

'I'm interested in you still, though I know you don't believe it. And when I knew we were coming this way, it seemed to be a good opportunity to look in. Besides, whether you believe me or not, I set store by your advice.' She paused, moved to face him head-on, opening herself to him. 'Do you ever feel you're throwing your life away?'

'That's common enough.'

'You and I,' she answered, creamily, as if with lines from a play, 'are in the same trouble. Neither actors nor critics are properly creative.' She waited. 'Except in some very small measure.'

'We both do work that I consider valuable,' he answered, flatly, the lawgiver. 'We are lucky.'

'In that thousands don't?'

'Or don't find it as interesting as we do. And if we're down

23

in the mouth about it from time to time. . . .' He shrugged, at her, at the human condition.

She considered him, not uncomfortably.

'You don't seem pleased to see me.' No answer. 'You're not very friendly. That isn't good. Or at least I . . . I can see that you look on me as an enemy who did you harm, and I can understand that. But I'm absolutely sure that it was for the best. Really so. Our life would have been a mess by now. There would have been constant quarrels and fights.'

Harrington struggled to keep his face straight. Sullenness rankled. The woman had no notion how she had damaged him.

'You're different, Joe.'

'Probably.'

'That was one thing I didn't like about you: the way you'd sulk if matters didn't go your way.'

He nodded in an exaggerated, ironical agreement. Paulina waited again, and receiving nothing, spoke but this time to the extended fingers of her left hand.

'What am I to do about the theatre, then?'

'I've no idea.'

'You're hopeless. You really are.' Mild exasperation at most, as if she held advantage.

'I've not seen you for three years. I've no means of assessing what has happened to you, what effects it has had, anything.'

'You knew whether I'd any talent.'

'You were talented,' he answered. 'You seemed ambitious. You'd go out of your way to do well. And you were selfish, prepared to trample over those who obstructed you. As I learnt. To my cost. I expect you're much the same now, but I don't know.'

'This isn't like you, Joe.' She softened her voice to wheedling. 'Are you not prepared to be friends with me?'

'No. I shan't put myself out.'

'Why did you answer my letter, then?' Sharply, ace of trumps.

'Curiosity. Stupidity. Politeness.'

24

She drew herself back from him without actually moving; she sat small, a threatened animal.

'Will you show me round your garden, then? That will be civilized?'

Harrington rose.

'Tell me about the house first. When it was built.' The voice purred into warmth. He led her out into the hall on a tour of inspection.

He explained that the house dated from 1905 when it was built for the manager of a pottery factory in the grounds of the squire's residence. Then it stood in fields a mile and a half away from the streets, and though the expansion of the town had been considerable, its favourable position had been protected by the erection of three large dwellings with extensive gardens, by allotments that had not been sold off and by the establishment of a spacious sports ground for the employees of a tobacco manufacturer and now owned by the education committee. His father had acquired the place, together with an adjacent plot of land when he had moved here during the last war.

'So this is where you were brought up?' Paulina asked.

'Until I was fourteen. Then my parents went back to London. And Alicia and her husband bought it. And I had it from them.'

'Where are they now?'

'Bournemouth. Gerald took early retirement.'

'And Alice is well? I liked her.'

His sister, ten years older than himself, married to a man fifteen years her senior, had got on splendidly, he had thought, with Paulina.

'Doesn't she write still?' he asked.

'No. We didn't give up immediately. It tailed off.'

He himself rarely wrote to Alicia.

As they walked, slowly in sunshine, round the garden he was surprised by her knowledge of the names of shrubs and plants. When he remarked on this, she said her father had been a keen gardener, and both of Edmond's houses had land.

'It never came up when we were married,' he muttered.

25

'We lived in a flat. We didn't know everything about each other.'

'No. We did not.'

She stared at him, but strolled on, determined not to clash.

'How did you learn the ins and outs?' she asked.

'Books. Catalogues. Talking with some of the men over in the allotments.' He pointed in that direction. 'Getting a good man in to help.'

'Yes. I see. Are you fit, Joe? Physically.'

'As ever I was.'

'You look a bit . . . slovenly.' She laughed, softening the criticism. 'Like a provincial university lecturer in a play.'

He considered this; certainly he had not changed from his working clothes. He cast his mind round his colleagues to find a sartorial stereotype, failed and did not therefore reply. As they progressed, at leisure, in full sunshine, she made suggestions for improvements in the layout of his land. Exchanges became almost animated because she showed sense, even flair.

On their return indoors, she sat down at once, moving her position so that she could look out into the garden.

'You were lucky to get this,' she offered. 'It's lovely.'

'Yes.'

'And you've settled down here?'

'Yes.' What else could he say?

'Are there prospects of moving?'

'One doesn't know. It's possible. I'm publishing things. I've contacts.'

'I bought your book,' she offered.

'And did you read it?'

'Yes.' Sadness sat about her. 'I remember when you were writing about Cowper's madness, how down you were. But in the book, it's clever and learned, and oh, polished.'

'You don't see me in it?' He laughed at her.

'I see you, but which you is it?'

'That's a point.'

Again she raised the matter of her theatrical career; again he refused to sound excited.

'I can't answer you. I can't see any good reason why you should give it up. But I haven't got the facts. If you're bored with the parts you're offered, or they don't challenge you as you expect, that doesn't seem reason enough to call it a day. While you're in the theatre, you'll be on hand, keeping your eye in, there to be summoned. But that's obvious enough to you. You don't need me to spell it out to you.'

She listened, tried listlessly to make him understand how full, interesting, demanding, important a life that of Edmond's helpmeet could be. It was conversation, not conviction; she evoked no real effort; neither person raised voice nor expectation. In the end she dropped the subject, saying Edmond would soon be back, demanded the bathroom and time to make up her face. As she rose she put her head to one side.

'I'm glad I've seen you.'

'This is what you've missed.' He waved his hand towards a trio of framed Athena prints.

'You weren't without your strengths.'

Paulina slipped out of the room, and was away for almost a quarter of an hour. Harrington sat uncomfortably, listening to catch her searching through his bathroom cupboard or dirty clothes bin. She reappeared, no more resplendent, just before Edmond rang the bell.

They did not dally. Paulina kissed him quickly, neat stage business; Lord Benson shook his hand, mind elsewhere, on his sick former chief clerk or his post-prandial platitudes to men of affairs. Harrington did not dislike him, not his excellent suit or shoes nor his confident voice; they could be friends except that they had nothing in common but this woman.

'Edmond read your book,' she gushed, out on the front-garden path. 'He thought it was brilliant.'

'It was very good,' he corrected. 'Not that I'm any expert, though I had to read Gray and Collins and Young and Smart at school.'

'Young and Smart,' she laughed. 'That would be you. Let me know,' she turned her face to Harrington, 'if you have any second thoughts. Lovely to see you again.'

27

They took to the car, which glided away. The street stood suddenly empty.

Back in the house Joseph Harrington looked about for change, and found none. He replaced Paulina's chair, handling it gingerly, afraid of taking the gloss off something he could not define. Ashamed of his own boorishness, angry at her curiosity or levity, he felt let down; the big event had turned out, as always for him, bathetic.

He ought now to resume work, but his mind seemed determined not to allow this. If he sat at his desk he'd be occupied within half an hour, but he could not take the first easy actions, of laying out books and paper. His head thumped with snatches of un-made conversation, pictures, conjectures; the colour red, an orange-red predominated, in a desert of continuous momentum. Like Wittgenstein he needed a cinema, a wall-sized huge screen and amplified voices to swamp the mêlée, medley, madly chaotic flurry that vamped round his head.

Harrington washed three cups, the tea pot, strainer, milk jug, before forcing himself upstairs to his books.

He did not work well, but he wasted no time.

4

Dr Helen Southwell knocked on the door of Harrington's study at the university, catching him at attention by his electric kettle. He had just finished a wearing tutorial, trying to screw words out of two schoolboyish clods and a pink-haired girl on the subject of Yeats's 'Sailing to Byzantium', a poem they had never seen before, and which, to judge from their pronouncements, might have been in Homeric Greek. Practical criticism. Neither word applied.

'Are you busy? Teaching?'

'No. Not till twelve.' He fished down a second mug.

'I want to ask you something. Where's Harry?' His room-mate, Dr Spellman.

'Not in this morning.'

She was a small woman, in her early thirties, pretty in her thin, nervous way, with large gig-lamp spectacles, on a tiny nose. Without hesitation she sat down in his chair, while he poured and stirred and complained about his pupils. Her pale face had already brightened. When he had perched himself at Spellman's desk, back to back with her, she swivelled his chair, looked at him over her glasses. The veins in her hands showed faintly purple.

'Would you mind,' she asked, 'if I came in here with you?'

'There isn't room.'

'No. Harry would move out.'

'Where?'

'To share with William in the new Education block.'

He considered. The advantage of sharing a room with Harry Spellman was that he was rarely in it; if he worked at all, it was in the library or the staff club. Helen would only be out when she ate or lectured.

'Does he want to go? He's not said a word to me.'

29

'He doesn't mind. Or so he says.'

'What's the advantage of all this, Helen? To you or me or anybody else?'

'Paul suggested it.' The professor. 'He said it would do me good to be in with somebody who finishes his work, gets it published.'

'And?'

'It might just come off. I'm desperate. My book ought to have been out years ago.' She smiled. 'I know what you'll say, that your presence won't make a ha'p'orth of difference, so we'd have the upset of shifting all these books . . .'

'That's so.'

' . . . and that it's Paul letting his tongue wag, again and without thinking as usual.'

'Right.'

'I'd like to join you in here.'

They discussed the colleague with whom she shared her present study, a crone aged barely fifty with a sniff and Directoire knickers who lectured on *Beowulf*. Helen had no fault to find there.

'No, I've nothing against Beatie. All she talks about is home decorating and the price of cornflakes, but she's kind. . . .'

'Won't she be upset that you want to desert her?'

'I hadn't thought of that.'

Helen launched into an account of her difficulties; lack of fluency played no part in her trouble, he thought, sipping. She flourished, then put down, half shifted her mug.

'What do you say, Joe?'

'I don't mind. If I were you I'd think about it, and delay the move to the Christmas holiday. I don't think it's the answer.'

Her face fell, like a child's. He soldiered on.

'Look, Helly. You're clever, probably the cleverest in the department. You're a worker, but you take on all sorts of chores the rest of us are too idle to do. You look after your students. You give this place value for money, and more. The only reason Wainwright nags you about your book is because he sees his teasing has some immediate effect. The best thing for you would be to type the Spenser thing up neatly to book length, and then get some well-intentioned expert to read it. Jack Clough. He'd do it for you. Or Spendlove at Leicester. I'll volunteer myself, when they've finished. Now what do you think?'

'You don't want me here?'

'You can come.'

She jumped up, snuggled against him. He patted her bottom. This was the sort of girl he should have married. He groaned inwardly. She thanked him, skedaddled out, leaving her mug three-quarters full. He wondered what she would be like at seventy, if she managed that far. Reaching for his books he forgot her inside ten minutes.

On his way to the car park he ran into Professor Wainwright who grumbled on about economies he was to make in his rock bottom budget. Harrington listened, and, as expected, heard again of the selfish stupidity of scientists. Wainwright loved to find a stick to beat his colleagues with. He appeared disgruntled, baffled, almost broken, but was in fact quite happy in that people had acted exactly according to his preconceptions, and this lifted, reassured him. Harrington thought the professor didn't much care how much was lopped off his book allocation, as long as it was accompanied by a speech from the professor of inorganic chemistry, an old antagonist, couched in predictable sentences.

'Well, I'll go home and grieve,' Wainwright said, unlocking his car.

'What's this about Helen moving in with me?'

The professor straightened; his hand fluttered upward from the keys, as if to defend his face.

'There was some talk,' he murmured. 'Isn't it a good idea?'

'Who suggested it?'

'Who? Well, now. Well. Who? She did, I think.'

'You approve?'

'These are not matters of prime importance, Joe. I don't care one way or the other. But if she thinks it will straighten her out, then. . . . I like to be of assistance.'

'Why should it?'

31

'Yes, you have me there. The crux is that you get things written and published. She doesn't. You might help her. I'd like to see her do well. She has real intelligence, Joe, an attribute in short supply in these parts.'

Wainwright darted at his handle, wrenched open the door, and was seated in his car in one clumsy movement. He had collapsed downwards, at the same time inserting his ignition key. Harrington was pleased to note that the man had difficulty in starting his engine, but the professor was modestly making self-deprecating gestures in his direction.

Harrington gave his senior time to rev his way out on full choke. He wondered if Helen Southwell had tendered the suggestion herself, though he hoped not. There was no pride in him now; he'd spoken to her as if she'd been an incompetent student. Pull your socks up. Ugh. Elevate your half-hose.

At home he filled a box with apples in his leisure hour and delivered them to the Selby back door. Anne appeared in outdoor clothes, explaining that she was about to visit her father. He offered to run her round; she did not argue at length. The children had been collected at school by a neighbour who would mind them until she returned.

'I like to look in on him,' she said. 'And this is the best way.'

She directed him to a suburban street of well-kept, small semi-detached houses, circa 1934, a journey of less than ten minutes.

'Will you come in?' she asked. The request in that bright social voice took him aback. 'I'd like you to. It'll put him on his best behaviour.'

They went round the back way, having difficulty with the catch on the latticework gate dividing the front from the yard. The house was unusual in that it had no garage, though an eight-year-old red mini stood in the drive.

Anne rapped on the back door, but made no attempt to enter. She tried again, no more loudly on the failure of the first summons. A thin, smart man in pullover, light blue shirt and cord trousers opened up; they heard in turn the Yale lock, two bolts, a chain, the rattle, no main key.

'Hello. I didn't expect you. I'd locked up for the night.' It was four-twenty.

'This is Dr Harrington who was kind enough to drive me round.'

'Glad to meet you.' Reeves looked wary, but shook hands. 'Come on in.' The finger poking at his closely trimmed moustache belied his smile.

The dining room into which he conducted them was square, with a table under the window, already laid with plate, cup and saucer, two knives presumably for high tea. A settee, a sideboard, and one open bookcase occupied the faded wall-to-wall carpet. A gas fire hissed in a hideous Art Deco glazed surround and hearth. The room seemed impersonal, as if the furniture had been bought carelessly at sales, or presented to a charity; nothing matched, but all was clean. There were no pictures on the walls, but over the fireplace three Gurkha kukris hung, tapering one above the other. Anne's father, at this late hour of the afternoon, still wore his slippers, of polished leather.

'It was Dr Harrington who provided me with all those apples,' Anne said, refusing refreshment, and as if to explain the visitor's appearance.

'Very good they were.'

They occupied the settee while Reeves sat eccentrically astride one of the dining chairs placed back towards them. He seemed not to be making any point by his position, to take it for granted that one swivelled a chair and straddled it. He uttered no horse-encouraging noises, aped no imaginary cavalry charge. His daughter rose, unpacked the bag of goodies she had brought, piling them on the table.

'She looks after me, this girl,' Tom Reeves said.

'Somebody needs to,' she answered.

She nagged about laundry, but he claimed that while his washing machine functioned properly she'd no need to worry her head. He did, however, after some negotiation hand over a Fair Isle pullover.

'You should get rid of that machine of yours and buy an up-to-date one,' she harried her father.

'And what shall I use for money?'

'You can afford it, as well you know.'

They continued the argument without rancour, as if it were much practised, a performance for Harrington's benefit rather than theirs.

'I don't suppose you have to suffer all this,' Reeves broke off to include the visitor.

'Dr Harrington lives on his own.' Anne quickly straightening it out.

'You're not married, then?'

'Divorced.'

'Yes. Well, there's a lot of it about.' The remark dropped oddly, as if conversation had exceeded propriety, and it silenced the three for some minutes before Anne rose, marched out to the kitchen where she could be heard opening and closing cupboards. Reeves nodded in that direction.

'She doesn't trust me to look after myself.'

'She calls in regularly?'

'Once a week without fail. Not more than twice.'

'And the children?'

'About once a month. With Tony. They come up to see a football match. Tony's interested in football, though I don't know why. Academically, you could say. He'd be no good at playing it.'

Again the awkwardness, the uncalled-for bile.

'Are you interested in the game?' Reeves asked, sunnily, redeeming himself.

'Not really.'

'No. There's nothing to it these days. The trouble is with professionals, any road, that they're too fit. They'll have to enlarge the pitch or reduce the number of players.'

Reeves spoke at speed now, knowledgeably, naming names; he and Tony Selby could well pass a productive hour on the topic.

'Did you play yourself?' Harrington asked.

'When I was young. Then this gammy leg put a stop to it.

34

The war.' He slapped one shin, and began to criticize an article he had read on the creative role of the goalkeeper in modern football. Harrington made answering noises, aware that Reeves was enjoying himself. What he said seemed sensible, even well-argued, certainly clear. 'I did a great deal of coaching. At school.'

'Why don't you write a letter to the newspaper? Put your ideas?'

'Waste of a stamp. They wouldn't print it.'

'But wouldn't it be good to get your ideas sorted out?'

'Do you think they aren't, then?'

Harrington flattered the man, but saw he had touched a wound.

'The trouble with print,' Reeves continued, apparently mollified, 'is that people pick on this word or phrase and make it different from what you meant. That's the real difficulty. And you're not there to clarify it at once, and then they get set in their ways. I've seen it time and again in letters in the *Guardian*. Not that I buy it every day.'

Helen Southwell could not have described her own dilemmas more clearly.

Anne returned.

'Don't you find that?' Reeves pursued.

'In my job you get used to it. It's called criticism.'

'Aren't you a medical doctor, then?'

Anne Selby and Harrington laughed; Reeves frowned, then joined them. When the daughter explained, the father breathed the word 'literature' with an ironic emphasis before shifting with sighs and heavy breathing to a more comfortable position across his chair.

'Try side-saddle,' Anne whispered in instruction. Reeves raised his eyes to heaven. 'Now, is there anything else you want, dad? I shall call in on Saturday morning because I have to come round this way to collect some stuff for Oxfam from the Misses Crippen.'

'No, I'm all right, thanks. I'm not helpless.'

He stood, but held on to the back of his chair, pleased with himself.

'What are you grinning at?'Anne demanded.

'Faded bloomers from antique faded limbs,' he rolled the words sonorously. 'The Crippens's gifts to the poor, Third World.'

Anne frowned, barely perceptibly, as a mother with a lively child in critical company.

'Oh, well,' she said. 'We'll go.' She motioned Harrington towards the door, but he shook hands with Reeves, sympathetic towards him.

On the drive back she said her father would have enjoyed the visit.

'I heard him while I was in the kitchen. It gave me half a chance to look round. He's like a lot of retired school teachers, he misses his captive audience. Since my mother left him he's been odder. And noisier. They'd been married nearly twenty years when she got out; I was fifteen, and Sally, my sister, eighteen.'

'You didn't go with her?'

'No. She just went off. To London. I don't blame her now, when I come to look at it. We girls were awkward, but just about ready to take care of ourselves.' Anne let her fingers paddle in her hair. 'He was worse. He hectored her. She could have been one of his backward class. He was a Japanese P.O.W. Worked on that Siamese railway. Not good, eh?' The last sentence might have come from her father's mouth.

'No.'

'It did something to him. Not that he talked much about it, not to us.'

'He'd be in his twenties then, wouldn't he?'

'That's right.'

'A poor way to start life.'

As she thanked him, she reached out to fondle his forearm, then quitted the car in a hurry, making not for her own front door, but down the street, presumably to the neighbour's house where she had left the children. She waved as he passed her, appearing not to look.

A week later, as he sat in his room at the university, Helen

36

Southwell again rapped on his door. It was ten past nine, and he had done a quarter of an hour's work.

'I take it you've heard,' she said, owl-faced, solemn.

'What?' He was not pleased.

'About Paul.' She seemed on the verge of disappearing.

'No. What about him?'

'He's in hospital.'

He waited for her to continue; she kept silence, standing inside, a yard away from the door.

'What's wrong with him?'

'He's had an accident in his car. Yesterday. On the main Costock road.'

'Is he badly hurt?'

'A broken leg. Crushed ribs. Cuts and bruises.' Her mouth remained open, as if she tried to force meaning out without making a sound. Her face was ashy. 'A boy was killed. His car mounted the pavement.'

'How did . . . ?'

'I don't know. Harold thinks it could have been a mechanical failure. Steering or tyres. It was a straight road. Not far from where he lives.'

'So he wouldn't be going very fast?'

'I don't know.'

'What time what this? Was it daylight?'

'Four o'clock. Yesterday was wet and dull. But he'd be able to see.'

'He wasn't drunk?'

'At that time? He went home early because he'd a meeting in the evening.'

'Is anybody going to visit him?'

'I thought I might. When we hear how he is. Jack Clough will ring the hospital, he says.'

'How did he find out?'

'The police phoned the university when they couldn't get a reply from Paul's home. The registrar told Jack. Rang his house first thing this morning, frightened his wife to death.'

Harrington worked badly, breaking off, stamping up and down the room. At eleven he, unusually, went across the

37

lawns to the staff club. Trees were almost stripped now, while yellow and red leaves clustered in lumpy swathes. He found no one from the English department; the professor of French had not heard of the accident, did not seem interested, stirring his coffee. On his return Harrington called in at Harold Morris's room, but withdrew at once as his colleague had launched into a tutorial. At lunch the accident was largely discussed, though nobody knew much. The hospital had confirmed that Professor Wainwright was comfortable and could be visited. The assistant registrar would drive over that afternoon. A boy had been killed. Voiced became instantly subdued, but chatter elsewhere cracked out as normal. Experts spoke of mechanical defects, inefficient garages; the speakers seemed selfishly pleased that they had escaped the consequences.

'He was not a good driver, hadn't much road sense.' A soul of tact from the German department. Silence fell; the young man blushed; knives clicked on plates.

'Let me know,' Harrington told Harold Morris, 'if there's anything I can do.' Morris looked affronted, bridling, knowing nothing. Harrington was pleased to get out, walk for half an hour on the autumn-rich campus.

A departmental rota of visits to hospital was drawn up by Helen, who put herself down to go along with Harrington on Friday evening. Paul Wainwright looked bad, his face cut and bruised. His left leg was broken, a wrist. After a first few minutes' cheerfulness, he relapsed into grim silence, his large yellow face twisting into grimaces of pain. He could by this time barely bring himself to answer their questions, and Harrington doubted whether the man listened to what his visitors said. Helen planned a visit to Rome this Christmas, was brushing up her Italian, was arguing with her travelling companion, a woman from the history department, about the best way of spending their time. Demure little Southwell revealed herself as one who knew her mind. Harrington said a word or two about his garden and his work on Yeats, but the professor ignored him, looking away, shutting his eyes. If Paul had begun to mutter to himself it would have been in character. Harrington then described how he was about to re-lay a flagged path with the help of his gardener, taking from his inner pocket a plan of the development. The professor, it is true, did receive the open papers in his hands and squint briefly at them, but gave the impression they were now imposing on him. Helen chirped questions, talked technical-ities, asked Joe why decisions had been made about a curve there, a shallower bend here; and at all times she tried to involve the invalid without distressing him. It was a brilliant little performance; Harrington had not realized how good a teacher his colleague was. Ideas flowed as she pushed searching questions on a subject in which she could have little interest, small knowledge. He did his best for her, and they talked over the awkward, sheeted body of the professor who had black chest hair growing right up to his shoulders. When at the end of half an hour Helen said that they ought to go now, Wainwright looked relieved, but composed his face to nod acquiescence.

'Is there anything you want?' she asked. Wainwright shook his head. The visitors took hold of his good hand; Dr Southwell straightened the sheet, earning herself a half-stifled groan from the patient.

'That was hard work,' Harrington said, once they were outside.

'It's the boy. I'm sure that's it. The one he killed.'

Clough had informed her, she continued, that there were witnesses who, according to the police, stated positively that Wainwright was not to blame. The child had dashed into the road. The motorist had swerved but still hit the victim and ended up demolishing a stone wall. The experts thought there had been a mechanical failure immediately after Wainwright had wrenched at his steering wheel. It was a complicated accident, still under adjudication.

'They say you should just brake,' Helen ventured, 'not try to swerve.'

'How old was the boy?'

'Nine.'

The age of Anne's elder child.

They parted in the hospital car park.

At the university on Saturday morning Harrington was stopped in the corridor by the registrar; a chicken stare, a brief nod, a choked greeting constituted the usual recognition.

'Have you been to see Professor Wainwright yet?' None of the casual use of first names for this man.

'Last night.'

'How did you find him?'

'I think he's improving. They said so. But he seemed very quiet.'

'Why would that be, d'you think?'

'Helen Southwell, who's seen more of him than I have, thinks it might be the death.'

'Possibly, possibly. One thing Wainwright dislikes is making a fool of himself.' The registrar, a feared man, wagged his jaw silently. 'Are you going to see him again?'

'Next week.'

'He's not likely to be out, is he?'

'There's no one to look after him at home.'

'You bachelors don't have all the advantages.' A bleak change of expression indicated that the registrar had indulged in a pleasantry. Harrington sycophantically smiled as the personage stepped away.

The inquest revealed that the boy had been exercising on a bicycle, had rolled slowly backwards after some one-wheel foolery on the pavement into the road where Wainwright had braked and swerved. The brakes had failed and the motorist, violently trying to avoid collision, had mounted the kerb, hit a wall. His speed had not been excessive; his car had received its M.O.T. certificate not a fortnight before; he had done all he could to prevent the accident. Death by misadventure. The coroner expressed sympathy with the parents and with the driver; a series of unfortuante incidents had culminated in the tragic death of this unfortunate and gifted child. Wainwright remained a few days in the hospital learning to walk with a frame, crutches, then a single stick.

When the professor returned home Helen Southwell moved herself into his house to care for him.

40

5

Paulina's silence did not surprise Harrington.

She had visited him out of curiosity, had made no headway and had forgotten him. This lack of social poise made an interesting topic of conversation, or exposition on his part, when Anne Selby dropped in. She had no real excuse; she had made a call in the area; the children were on their weekly visit to the neighbour; she wondered how he was.

Harrington, not altogether pleased to see her in that it might make the start of his evening's work more sluggish, noticed her interest at a mention of his ex-wife change when it became clear that they were talking about Paulina Street, the television star. He felt disappointment that this should be so, expecting, for no reason, something better of Anne Selby. She had the limitations of her age and class; a cooped-up housewife, who knew no university teachers except him, suddenly found that he was connected with a public figure. He guessed that she kept back a thousand and one questions, and wondered whether when she fetched her children she would raise the name of Paulina Street with her neighbour.

They went round the house together, then the garden. Anne expressed surprise at his neatness.

'This isn't an easy place to keep clean,' she averred. 'These old houses never are. There are too many holes and corners. But I can see you flick a duster about, and use your vacuum cleaner. And you don't abandon things. If Tony's finished with a newspaper or book he just drops it at his feet on the floor. And leaves it for me to pick up. The boys are as bad. I tell him that I've no chance of training them with the example he sets.'

Anne Selby personified neatness in herself, looked pretty,

41

well dressed but was boring. Paulina made a difficult act to follow.

He shooed Mrs Selby out, though he had been, in the end, glad to see her. There was a lilt, a rhythm about her talk, he thought; he must try tape recording her conversation to see if second or third hearings confirmed the findings, or whether they were a secondary result of a smart, young woman descending on him without pressure on his part. Her neat legs and ankles, her white, elegant hands would have graced an advertisement hoarding. The regular features, greenish eyes and old-fashioned fair hair gave her an appearance of authority, so that her smiles, hesitations, peekings seemed out of character. Here stood, he felt, someone who had tested experiences he had not even approached. Why did he indulge in such jaunts of the imagination? A suburban housewife with a few minutes of leisure on her hands chose, because her other options were dull, to spend time in his company. In his study he pulled down his books to wrestle with Blake.

Helen Southwell, sister of mercy, had sounded cheerful all day.

From moment to moment, twice a week perhaps as she was a sensible woman, she reported to Harrington on Wainwright's progress. Nothing, it appeared, gave the professor more pleasure than describing the university twenty years ago, in the swinging sixties, when he had first been appointed to the chair of English.

As far as Harrington could gather from other older members of the staff the seeds of revolution had fallen on stony ground in these parts: there had been many noisy meetings, from which the majority of students stayed away. Two sit-ins had done some damage in the administrative block; the vice chancellor had called for a police investigation, and the students' union had made financial reparation. One assistant lecturer in the sociology department had not, after some accusation and counter-thrust reported in the local newspaper, been reappointed. Banners, slogans and posters proliferated. Marches were less evident. The vice chancellor and registrar had both been faced, shouted at without much result in their offices by young men and women with Marxist views. The student newspapers bubbled and frothed, but lectures and laboratories were well-attended. The present registrar, then a mere assistant, gave it now as his opinion that their peculiar mixture of Home Counties female bourgeoisie with men hacking their way out of the Northern or Midland working-class streets had been too canny or apathetic by a large half for Mao's *Little Red Book* or schemes of radical reform. 'True,' the registrar's bored lawyer's voice droned, 'some people perhaps did not quite slog it out for the first or upper seconds they might have gained in happier times, but . . . I say "true,", but it's not truth, that's wrong; it's impression.' The rate of abortions rose; there were more dropouts than is the case today. 'But I tell you this,' the registrar continued, expecting his every syllable to be noted, 'if you get hold of the files of the university papers, and pick out the names of the big bawlers for change, and then chase up their subsequent careers you'll find them, twenty years on, holding down exactly the jobs in industry or the professions you'd have expected if there had been no disruption. All of which goes to show.' The registrar did not explain what he meant. Harrington's unexpressed interpretation was that students didn't know their minds, were better occupied with essays or experiments, and that as long as administrators stood no nonsense, silkily, politely, all manner of thing would be well.

Or, as Harold Morris put it, after the registrar had gone, 'It was a dull hole then as it's a dull hole now.'

Harrington had the impression that Professor Wainwright and Helen filled every evening with talk of the brave old days. Paul, her voice grew both shriller and quieter, had at bottom sympathized with the students, who had right of sorts on their side. This seemed barely believable. At bottom, where fathom line could never touch the ground, unless Wainwright at forty cut a different figure from that of the sixty-odd-year-old, the professor would line up with authority, the V.C., the registrar, the dean of engineering or his equivalent at that time. Of course, Helen reported, some of the students were silly; there was too much money about in that they all spent

43

the long vac in gainful employment instead of at their books or on mind-broadening travel, but their views on peace, on freedom, on the removal of shackles, parental, religious or patriotic, were to be applauded. These youngsters wanted a new world, bright with independence, lifted with pop music, where the old, the grudging, the niggler, the competitive neurotic had no part; we are all equal in the eyes of no-God. Elitism would disappear; with war condemned, loving made new, sex liberated, women free, drugs tolerated, prejudice banished, the world would run oiled like a thrilling roller coaster.

Neither Harrington nor Helen Southwell remembered anything but the fag end of these days, but both argued against the Wainwright exposition. This led Paul, she reported, who was not making the progress with walking he should have done, who hated his physiotherapist and refused to do his exercises at home, to a further piece of theoretical thinking.

These radicals of the sixties were the Tories of today, in positions of importance, poised to take over, already infiltrating the offices of power, influential in politics, the media, industry, science, education. And their radicalism had coloured their Conservatism. Now they wanted freedom from governmental interference, from the paternalist state. They would make their pile, put their children into public schools, suffer their illnesses in private wards, buy their own estates, provide for old age and see to it that everyone, free as birds, could do likewise. They found no paradox in this, any more than they had grasped the untenable tenets of their student claims. The great British, English compromise had succeeded flower power, and such workers as held down jobs saw the sense of it all.

That Wainwright theorized at length about politics surprised Harrington who guessed that a few, mainly grumbling, remarks had been extended and smoothed by Helen into some sort of system. On the few occasions the younger man visited his professor, Wainwright shuffled and groaned and complained. Even Helen's efforts on his behalf were condemned.

'She's like all women. Wants it laid on the line. "Make your mind up or I'll make it up for you." '

'Is she a good cook?'

'She provides meals, certainly. Yes.'

Helen had confided, not without acid, an account of bathing the patient. Wainwright was awkward physically when fit, but in plaster and stark naked he excelled himself.

'I scrubbed him,' she said, 'till he was red.'

'Did he holler?'

'He does nothing else.' Helen dropped her eyelashes into mock modesty. 'I didn't know where to look.'

'You're a saint.'

Though the professor occupied so much of her time, she seemed to come to terms with a first draft of her book on Spenser. Jack Clough, the reader, had approved the first two completed chapters, which were passed to Harrington for his opinion. They were learned, highly intelligent and enlightening.

'This is the best piece of criticism I've read this year,' he said drily. 'I might even try to read Spenser again.'

She threw her arms round his neck.

'Swilling Wainwright's private parts down has done you good.'

She reddened, kissed him and landed a left into his ribs, rather too hard.

Anthony Selby rang the university one day for a select list for his library on structuralism, the post-structuralists, the theory of deconstruction, 'something straightforward, if that's possible.' Harrington said he would oblige, but Selby seemed unwilling to get off the line.

'There is one other thing.' He sounded as if he whispered.

'What's that then?'

'It's a private matter. I can't talk about it over the phone.'

'Will it take long?'

'I shouldn't think so.'

They arranged to meet that lunch hour and take a turn in

the university park. Harrington was waiting among the cars when the other drove up. The pair slapped it along a tarmac lane under horse chestnuts, bare now, when Selby began.

'This is a bit embarrassing, really.'

Harrington did not answer, banging one foot down after another.

'But I thought I ought to mention it. It's about Anne. She calls in to see you?'

'Occasionally.'

'You don't mind?'

'No. She's considerate of my time.'

'She comes to talk to you, would you say?'

'I never thought of it. She's not been often enough. I wasn't sure whether she was filling in spare minutes, or whether she wanted to keep an eye on me, to check if I was looking after myself properly.'

'Properly,' Selby repeated. 'I'm not suggesting that there's anything improper.'

Harrington bit back a sarcasm, kept walking.

'It's like this,' Selby did not slow his stride. 'I wondered if she was getting, well, becoming obsessed with you.'

'What makes you ask that?'

'You appear in every conversation. Dr Harrington thinks, says, does.'

'I see. Is this unusual behaviour? Does she tend to latch on to a person, or a topic?'

'I hadn't noticed it.'

'And you feel yourself threatened in some way by this?'

Selby swerved at the question, came to a standstill, stood scraping his sole on the edge of the kerb.

'I'm not accusing you of anything,' he answered.

'I didn't suppose you were, but presumably Anne's behaviour in this respect is bizarre enough to cause you to raise the matter with me.' His own choice of vocabulary was not faultless.

They set off to walk again, but more slowly as if prepared on reaching a point of crisis to halt.

'I don't know,' Selby began. 'Your house, your ideas, even

46

your apples are models, perfection. I don't like it. I wouldn't quite use your word, "threatened", but I feel uneasy. Wouldn't you?'

'That would depend entirely on what I knew about her.'

The wrong answer, delivered from on high, flooring both.

'She's a good wife, a good mother.'

'But bored?'

'That comes into it, I'm sure. But now both boys are at school, she's doing a bit of home teaching. The money's handy, and it fills the time. She attends a morning class on psychology once a week.'

'It's no part, I mean. . . .' Harrington broke off.

'Yes?'

'I was going to ask a question or two, but I see. . . .'

'Go ahead. That's sensible.'

'But I'm one of the parties concerned.'

The sky stretched uniform grey, though the weather was not cold. Fog smudged distant trees and buildings; the air hung clammy.

'Say your piece,' Selby ordered, in good humour.

'Let me assure you that there's nothing between your wife and me. She has called in twice or three times, has stayed no more than half an hour. I was, I am, considering asking your family over for lunch. That's the total situation.' He broke off. 'I suppose that's just what I'd say if we were having an affair. But we are not. I thought your wife was being neighbourly, or occupying a spare few minutes. She tells me what you and the boys are doing and makes inquiries how I fill my day in. Flatly. Unemphatic. Normally. If she comes away from these visits talking about my house or life, at unreasonable length or with, oh, vehemence, then it surprises me, and I'd begin to think the rest of her life was abominably dull. She seems a level-headed woman to me.' He was breathless after this speech which he delivered in sentence lengths, with pauses to allow intervention.

'Are you suggesting that I'm misreading the situation?' Selby asked.

'That's not for me to say.'

47

'I'm not a jealous man. At least I think I'm not. And, as far as I understood it, we were going along well. We've been married eleven years. But your name comes up too often. "I wonder what Dr Harrington would say about that." ' The voice took on no overtones of femininity or irony. 'It's worrying.' Selby pushed at his sleeve to consult his watch. 'I shall have to be getting back.'

'Have you had any lunch?'

'Apple. Cup of coffee. Y'know.' He sounded shamefaced.

'This way.' Harrington led him across a rising lawn.

'You don't mind my seeing you about this?'

'Why should I?'

'If she visits you again, I'd be grateful if you wouldn't mention this, this talk we've had.'

'Why not?'

'Leave it to me. I may have misjudged the situation entirely, as you suggest.'

'Won't you talk to her about it?'

'I'll see. I don't want to cause needless trouble.'

They were descending a grassy hillock at a fast pace, a near-stumbling run that precluded talk. A hundred yards of road, taken in silence, brought them to the car park. Selby put out an ungloved hand.

'Thanks for listening to me. I may have got it round my neck.'

The man looked sane enough, in his belted mackintosh. They shook hands and Harrington immediately made off. Once inside where the warm corridors echoed to his footsteps, he faced his unease. He categorized Tony Selby as one to make something out of nothing, who stirred the waters because of his own inadequacies. It did not quite fit. And yet he'd begun to write Anne off as a dull subordinate.

'Out for a walk?'

A small dark figure clipping downstairs greeted him. Emrys Morris-Jones.

'Yes. It's not cold.'

'I'm frightened of getting my feet wet.'

Morris-Jones did not stop, stepped neatly below, Celtic,

dark-maned with a pale skin. Kate, his wife, had called round one summer Saturday afternoon on Harrington, having sat with him the night before at a hall dinner, accepted a gin and tonic, had pulled him to her, flung up the crimson skirts of her dress, the only garment she wore, and dragged him to the carpet. Face composed after coitus, she had demanded a cup of tea, very large and milky. She had then talked with an intelligent cheerfulness about some problems in the philosophy of history that puzzled and occupied her husband. When Harrington offered to cut her a bunch of flowers from his garden, she refused, guffawing. The affair, if it were that, lasted four months. She would telephone, arrive, name her tipple, screw, talk, fall on him again, try his tea, grab him until the end of her time with him, never more than three hours. A clever woman, she looked on sex as a marvellous bubbling therapy, and though she protested love for him – she gabbled endearments without break in their bouts – he never thought of her, once dressed and upright, as other than a casual friend.

The end came as unexpectedly as the start.

'I shan't see you any more,' she said, china cup raised. 'I think Emrys has found out.' Harrington, stunned, for their sexual exchange ten minutes earlier had been as violently successful as before, could not believe it. 'You've done me more good than I can tell you, but it's no use ruining domestic life. Neither you nor I want that.'

He had protested, but she'd told him to think and not to make a nuisance of himself. Why she had acted as she did, he never decided; presumably her excuse, feeble as it appeared, carried as much likelihood as anything else.

Kate called round on him once more, to return a book of Doris Lessing short stories she had lifted without his knowledge from his shelves. She cheerfully repulsed the pass he made at her, aiming a haymaker that stopped an inch or two short of his genitals.

'Down, wanton, down,' she quoted, and confided to him how she hated the winter, lived for the spring. She turned as she was about to leave. 'You're one of the few people in this

49

bloody university with anything about him. That means, I suppose, you'll be off soon.'

'Who are the others?'

'Not Saint Paul Wainwright.'

They laughed out loud. He had savagely missed her infrequent afternoons, but now felt, as the pair of them, pleased with themselves, hugely grinning, looked out through the open door to his winter pathways, that he had avoided some dangerous choice. She invariably made for him at social functions; their exchanges were admired. Even Morris-Jones commented that Kate had said that in the four minutes' grace before nuclear warheads exploded, if only conversation were allowed, she would choose to spend the time with Joe Harrington. 'I can feel intelligent and giggle, both.' Morris-Jones reported this in his flattest voice, dangling high-held hands like a cartoon rabbit; no way, he considered, to prepare for eternity.

Harrington reached his room; the couple of students he expected at two o'clock were already there.

'Am I late?' he asked.

'No, we're early; we're keen.'

He scowled.

6

Harrington spent Christmas in Budapest.

A young man in the History department, Tom Firth, had stopped him in the corridor, coughed and asked if he'd like to accompany him there in the place of some Cambridge don who'd dropped out. From their hotel in the Lenin Körút near the Nyugati Pályaudvar they'd trotted off each breathless day. Firth, who had a smattering of most European languages, tried his tongue out on Hungarian. Harrington enjoyed their week in the wintry, glittering city where notices and exchanges in the street were incomprehensible; the two watched a football match and Firth ski-ed on the nursery slopes of Szabadsághegy while both skated in the Town Park; they ate modest, delicious meals, drank dark Hungarian beer, cold as the air outside, ventured into the pastry shops, tasting the barack. Time passed quickly, pleasantly and Harrington by the end of the week was coming to terms with his own ignorance and his companion's boldness. He had imagined useful traipses round museums and art galleries; Firth, against expectation, delighted in landing them in some place where they needed explanation or directions and there tried out his German, basic Russian, twenty-two words of Hungarian. It exhilarated in that they found themselves in interesting situations, were never completely lost, were not arrested though once they attracted a laughing crowd, not a word of English between them, on the Marx Square, a few minutes' walk from their hotel. Their shoes were much admired.

Back at home, Harrington found that his central heating had protected the pipes from freeze-up though flurries of snow threatened this cold New Year. At the university, Helen Southwell had moved her books into his office, all neat and square, with her box files and a high writing table, like a

51

conductor's stand, at which she sat on a tall three-legged stool to work.

She fished pleasantly for his views of Hungary; his card of the National Museum arrived well after his return. She reported that Professor Wainwright was now clearly on the mend.

'Are you still living there?' he asked. She blushed, dabbing hair from her face.

'Of course not. I've more sense than that.'

He learnt before too long that she was having trouble with her landlady about her present rooms and she was considering buying a house.

'Won't they give you a place in a Hall somewhere? Wainwright ought to be able to fix that.'

'I don't want it. And I don't want to be indebted to him.'

'You haven't quarrelled, have you?'

'That's ridiculous. But he's getting better, and will have to learn to fend for himself.'

She'd completed Chapter Three of her Spenser book, but had now stopped work.

'Why, in heaven's name?' Harrington pressed her.

'I lack the will.'

'You need to be washing Wainwright's balls down to spur you on.'

She looked nearer tears than laughter. In return for ribaldry he read the chapter before it went off to the experts. It was not only immensely learned, she had read widely in three foreign literatures and was much at home with the history of the period, but entertaining. Her anecdotes made the book readable; her critical commentary livened. Here a highly intelligent mind worked at pressure but without ostentation. Harrington looked the slim woman over, disregarding her diffidence, the flitting smile; her brain was a powerful dissecting instrument, and with her sensibility and concentration made her formidable. If she completed the book she would have written a critical masterpiece, a piece of literature in itself.

When he said as much, she backed away, fiery red, wept

brief tears and swept out incapable of enjoying the praise with the one who delivered it. On the next day, she asked in case of her landlady's playing awkward whether he could put her up until she had bought a house.

'What scandal,' he mocked. 'First you move in with Paul, then with me. What will people say?'

'Does it matter?' Why did she take him seriously?

'Does it now? To whom? we ask ourselves.'

'You've plenty of room. I shan't be a nuisance.'

'Will you give me a bath?' He felt immediately ashamed to have spoken thus.

'Oh, Joe. Be serious.'

'I'll think about it.'

At the beginning of term he met Wainwright hobbling out of the library. The professor made an art of his disability, wielding his stick with awkward delicacy and matching his face to the pain. He stopped Harrington imperiously with his head, both hands being occupied.

'How was Prague?'

'Budapest.'

'Yes. If you say so.'

Harrington offered him three enthusiastic sentences, two more than the professor required.

'I hear Dr Southwell's moving in with you.'

'I didn't know. When?'

'Don't be a fool, Joe.' A rictus of pain afflicted the face, but he explained himself. Harrington answered graciously; the senior man waved his stick to signal relief.

'Have you read her stuff on Spenser yet?' Harrington asked.

'She's started to write, then?'

'Why, didn't you know? She did at least one chapter while she was looking after you.'

'She never said. She's a secretive little thing. Or am I wrong?'

'You haven't seen it?'

'No. No. Should I? I had the impression that you thought I harried Helen too much on that subject. Now I haven't done enough. There's no pleasing you young men.'

'Read it.' Harrington spoke as if dismissing a student.

'I will. I will. Not that I'm any expert on Spenser. And I shall not be much use to her in judging critical ability or intuitions or sensibility or the application of these, these modern theories about discourse. My line is old-fashioned scholarship, and this is a period about which, I regret it, but, I am sadly ignorant these days.' Wainwright swayed as if the confession increased the pain in his limbs.

'You ought to recognize quality when you see it.'

'Not easy, Joe, in topics about which one knows little. Could you pick out the best in wine, or even yoghurt or prize leeks? You're not in love with the girl, are you?'

'Never mind my motives.'

'You've not answered my question.' Wainwright bared large, yellow teeth.

'No. Sorry, but no. It's her work I admire.'

'Her mind.' Had the idiot misheard? 'In which case be careful. That's the worst.' He gathered books, stick, tattered nerves, battered legs together and hobbled rapidly away.

Harrington rushed into the library, annoyed by his annoyance. He ought to set about his boss, or at least to praise Helen Southwell with more power. Was it that he would one day need his professor's recommendation if he decided to move elsewhere? He despised the man, and yet Wainwright had produced a work of scholarship that had lasted over thirty years of critical change and was still useful. How many professors had done that? Perhaps it was that he had worked in a period where few had exerted themselves, where critical exchange was the exception rather than the rule, where actual knowledge was limited in a way that did not apply to more modern texts. Whatever it was. Whatever.

He passed the library barriers, returned a book, made his morning's demands, idly scanned the dust covers of new publications by members of the staff in a display cabinet. A new edition, with a chaste illustration from some medieval manuscript, of Wainwright's book held its own amongst titular jargon, mathematical wit and scientific unintelligibility. In just over a year's time his primer on Yeats would stand

54

crisply there, though his Frost was conspicuously absent. He moved resolutely towards his studies.

One morning at home the telephone rang as he was packing his bags for work. He felt particularly pleased because an editor from a distinguished publishing house had written pressing him for a small book on Romanticism in a highly praised series. The right people began to recognize him. If he finished the Yeats before the summer term ended, a distinct possibility now, he could use the long vac for the new project. It was possible. He had none of Helen Southwell's inhibitions; his books need not be potboilers, nor need they be full of error or glaring omission. Clarity would be his aim; to show right-minded students the distant shining light or wicket gate. That was why he was here, a teacher, an instructor, an evangelist; he did not reject the names, the mission.

Mr Reeves, Anne's father, telephoned his house.

'I've written something down, and I wonder if you would read it.'

'What sort of thing?'

'My experiences. Mainly as a prisoner of war. In time.'

'You want me to look it over with a view to publication?'

'Now that's going a bit far. I want you to look it over. Stop. Annie said I should ask you.'

'What sort of state is it in?'

'State? It's not typed. But the first part's neatly written out. I mean I did it on bits and scraps. But now I've done this piece neatly.'

'Is it complete?'

'By no means.' Reeves chuckled phlegmily. 'No, I've just about got myself out of the secondary school. With matriculation exemption, Higher School Certificate.'

'Mr Reeves.' Harrington held up further reminiscence. 'There's a question I'd like to put to you. Why are you writing this?'

'Why does anybody write anything?' Again the chesty laugh, as if he'd checked a cunning opponent. 'But, y'know, I've had some interesting things happen to me. It might be valuable as history. Anne thought. . . .' He left it there.

55

'Has she read it?'

'She has not.'

'How long is it?'

'About thirty sheets of foolscap up to pres.'

'Well, get it into a legible form, and I'll look at it.'

'If you're very busy just at present. . . .'

'I've said I'll read it.'

Reeves coughed eloquently, thanked him, rang off.

Three days later Anne appeared with a brown paper parcel from her father. Harrington had not seen her since her husband's visit to the university. He had dropped the idea of inviting the family over for a meal, or the parents over for a drink, but had compromised on a Christmas card, scribbled off before he left for Hungary. Their returned greetings, an afterthought, awaited his return from the Continent.

Anne, sitting, looked bright, pleased to be there.

'What do you think about this, then?' He tapped the parcel.

'I haven't read it.'

'No. The idea. Does it surprise you?'

'He's an intelligent man. He had a grammar school education up to eighteen. Then training college. He can write a good letter or a narrative if he puts his mind to it.'

'But he's not done anything similar before?'

'No. He was a disappointed man. He felt, perhaps rightly, that but for the war, and what happened to him there, he might have ended as managing director of a firm, instead of a teacher. It made him jealous of Sally and myself. We had opportunities he'd never had; he sacrificed for us as his parents had not done for him; we didn't make the most of our chances. De-dah, de-dah.'

'And your mother?'

'She stuck it longer than I would.'

'This will be his kick at the hard world?' He tapped the parcel.

'I wouldn't be surprised.' She smiled, arranged herself for more pleasant topics. 'Now he's retired I suppose it gives him something to do.'

'How did he use his spare time before?'

'Watching telly.'

Harrington picked the parcel up, weighed it in one hand.

'Yours wasn't a very happy childhood?' He risked that.

'No, it wasn't.' Anne braced herself. 'But I don't want to make too much of it. Children are quick enough to saddle themselves with sorrows. He wasn't physically cruel to us. But he and my mother were at loggerheads, and she'd use us as a stick to beat him.'

'Where do your sympathies lie?'

'With my mother. Obviously.'

'But you still visit him? Send the children up there?'

'He's my father. But,' she both smiled and bridled, 'what's all this to do with . . . ?' She pointed at the parcel.

'This idea that one should know something about the writer's life as well as the poem or novel one's reading is coming into favour again.'

She pulled a sour, father-like face at the foolishness of academics, who could only now and then accept or preach what common-sensical laymen knew all along to be the truth.

They talked for a few minutes, but when she rose to go to collect her children she said, and her voice was restrained,

'My husband came to see you, didn't he? One lunch time at the university?'

'Yes.'

'About me, wasn't it?'

'I think I can admit that.'

'He'll have to watch his step.'

Harrington did not reply to this bitterness and although she paused, staring at him, as if waiting for a response, it was not for long. She let herself out without another word.

He read Reeves's manuscript late that evening. It was a grammatically sound, even literary piece of work, from one brought up on Robert Lynd or *Alpha of the Plough*. The main concern was with education; the spinsters in the infant and Sunday schools were described; the teachers in the junior department; the gowned masters in the secondary school. The occasional Anglican or nonconformist parson made an appearance; prizes were handed out, the public library where both the dragon at the desk and the caretaker viewed him with suspicion was visited, and authors were named: Conan Doyle, Henty, Westerman, Hope, Lion Feuchtwanger, Scott, Orczy, Kipling. There were walks in propriety in public parks; success in cup ties in football and cricket competitions was mentioned. The wireless made a contribution to expanding knowledge. The boy had enjoyed trips to Stratford-upon-Avon, to the County Cricket Ground, to Newstead Abbey.

Harrington found this not without interest but disappointing. The detail convinced, but the manner seemed impersonal. Reeves's parents flitted in and out, but they were shadowy even compared with Mr T. B. Rice-Smith, sometimes scholar of Trinity College, Oxford, who taught young Tom for mathematics in his third year. Sex went unmentioned; according to this no girls distracted the boy from the improvement of his mind; his knees were never dirty even on the games field nor his clothes torn. It all sounded unlikely, too prim, written to point a moral, unconnected with the sour man whose wife had left him, whom the Japanese had starved. Reeves could have done worse by depicting himself as a rip-stitch, a fly-by-night, poaching, fornicating or vandalizing; even in this mealy-mouthed account he did not exactly boast, but the tone struck uniformly pious, if not hypocritical. The writer concealed himself; the style smelt of damp and mothballs.

Harrington put it to one side.

A day or two later, in a term gathering impetus, and January unappetizing with sleeting rain, Helen Southwell shook off rain hood and cape, giggled into speech.

'I've got something to tell.'

'Scandalous?'

'So-so. But you must promise not to say or do anything about it.'

He grunted; it was Monday morning, unpleasant, with his sinuses scraped raw.

'Oh, well,' she said. 'Paul warned me not to move in with you.'

'Go on.'

'He told me, humming and hawing, that you had the reputation of a lady's man. And he made a pronouncement. "Don't go there unless you love him." It was touching, really. Don't you agree?'

'Perhaps he fancies you for himself.' Grumps.

'I don't think so.'

'Are you going to pay any attention to what he says?'

'No. It seemed so funny. He was embarrassed. "You know Helen, I look on sex, well differently, probably, from the way you do. For me, it's not a merely physical act, a pleasure taken, as it were, *in vacuo*." ' The imitation, in spite of her high voice, steered close to reality.

'Has he ever talked to you like this before?'

'No.'

'Your time as his nurse changed all that.'

Harrington returned to his letters as if the subject were exhausted.

'Did he ask you about your Spenser?'

'No.'

'Silly bastard.'

Helen, back to him, breathing heavily began her day's work, but as she went out for a ten o'clock class, she piped up again.

'You won't say anything to Paul will you?'

'Not a word.'

He did not look at her, though he felt slightly aggrieved at Wainwright's presumption. Presumably the man referred to the affair with Eustacia Bates, a research student, now teaching (with success) at the Middlesex Poly. The pair of them had raised a few eyebrows, when Eustacia boasted round the campus of her conquest. She was bright in every sense, from clothes to features, from scholarly theory to powers of argument, epistemology to sexual mores; if there had been justice she would have been appointed to an assistant lectureship in the department, but Wainwright and Jack Clough, the reader, had picked out for themselves some dim dumbo from Oxford. Harrington wondered whether his association

59

with Stacey had scotched her chances; a possibility. And this from Wainwright who praised the promiscuous sixties, but whose mind now moved with ponderous irony to lay blame for contemporary Toryism on the earlier wild capers of its middle-aged supporters.

Cold rain misted the windows. He glowered down at the flat roof and skylights of the extended floor below. Not a good wash day for Anne Selby. Nor for Helen's titbits. Nor for W. B. Yeats. He filled his kettle. At least the authorities kept the lecturers' room near blood heat.

7

John Joseph Harrington, M.A., Ph.D., sorted through his Christmas cards before he amended his list and slung them into the dustbin. He ought to pass them on to some charity or infant school, could not be bothered to inquire how. Paulina and her husband had not favoured him with a greeting, but he left their name in his book. He rang Anne Selby to report that he had read her father's manuscript twice.

'What's the best way to get it back to him? Shall I post it, or deliver it, or will you or he fetch it?'

'I'll inquire, and let you know.'

She put down the phone, apologizing that she was in the middle of the campaign to get the boys to bed, as Tony was out. She did not question him about the quality of the work.

Helen Southwell had reported that a room had been found for her in one of the halls of residence, where in return for meals and accommodation she'd act as moral tutor to students. Harrington inquired whether Wainwright had arranged this for her, but found it not the case. She'd spoken to Evelyn Hughes, the warden, a woman younger than herself, who'd been glad to fix it in no time for her.

'Why haven't you done this before?' he asked her.

'I lived in a hall when I first came. Then I thought I ought to spend some time outside the university.

'You're not looking for a house any longer?'

'I don't know about that.'

She was too busy, he knew, with lectures and tutorials to work seriously on her Spenser, but the pause might be to her advantage. She proved an ideal roommate, always considerate, leading off the importunate for treatment in the stockroom at the end of the corridor. He warned her about wearing herself out on trivialities.

'It's what I'm paid for.'

'You take too much on yourself. Because the rest of us are selfish or idle, you get landed with all the emotional cripples.'

'Somebody has to. I don't want to end up another Jack Clough.' Clough, the reader, unlike Wainwright, had maintained at least a show of his earlier cleverness, still read a great deal, was an exacting critic when he applied his mind, but would not put himself out for a student. In departmental meetings he sometimes made a principle of his apathy. 'Look, they have too much done for them already. This isn't a nursery school. If they're any good they'll find their way through. I can't think of any intervention by teachers on my behalf which brought me the slightest advantage. Rather the opposite.'

Helen argued against him. Clough smiled drily; women differed from men.

'I sometimes wish it was the bigger causes,' she told Harrington, 'I was involved in, so that I would know I was right. Such as world peace or starvation-relief.'

'That's the first step towards Cloughery.'

She laughed out loud.

'And yet he's been very good over my book.'

'Just now and then, and if he can do it without too much disturbance, he likes to test himself out, to see whether his brain has atrophied or not. He also realizes that you're clever, and he wants to impress you. And there's Jack Clough written off for you.'

'You do me good.'

'I tell you the things you want to hear.'

'You're as bad as he is.'

Late one afternoon at the end of January he was surprised when Helen burst into their room. Usually she did not appear on Friday, a free day, preferring to work in the hostel or the main library.

'I've come in for a book,' she excused herself. He grunted, pleasantly. The last of the essays on Wordsworth lay open on his desk, half-marked; this time at least the students had paid attention to his instructions. A quarter of an hour would see him out of the place.

'Have you five minutes to spare?' she asked. He spun round in his chair at the tense voice.

'For you.'

She did not smile; she seemed puzzled, as if groping for words or topic. She neither approached her desk nor sat on one of the spare seats.

'I'd like your advice.' Still, small voice; trace of a frown in the clear skin over the nose.

'Is it a cup of coffee job?' He did not hide his good humour.

'No. Sit where you are, Joe.'

She leaned with an arm stretched against the upright of a bookshelf. Her hand slipped; two books were pushed inwards. She twisted her head to read their titles, but did nothing to straighten them. Surprise that the books had moved seemed dominant.

'Joe. It's like this.' The few words exhausted her. 'Joe, Paul has asked me to marry him.' Silence.

'And what did you say?'

Helen waved her hands in front of her chest to conjure breath for her answer.

'I didn't know what to. . . .'

'I see. Well, give us the circumstances, then.'

'He came out of the refectory at much the same time as I did, and invited me to walk back with him. I was surprised because he'd not been sitting with me, and he usually goes off with the registrar. But while we were outside – we came the long way round, in spite of his lameness, by the David Merrit Hall – he just made conversation.'

'About what?'

'He's been invited to a conference in Durham. He made it sound interesting.'

'And?'

'When we came to the main entrance of the Marshall building I was going to go on to come up here, but he asked me if I could spare him a moment. . . . In his room. . . .'

'When was this?'

63

'Yesterday. Thursday. He put his keys to the door and then inquired how my work was going. I said a few words and he – and you know how he walks just ahead or behind you and talks to the ceiling – told me that both you and Jack Clough thought very highly of it. "And they have nothing in common but brains." ' Harrington could hear the breathy sentence behind her imitation. 'We stood outside his room, and you know how he fiddles with his keys as if he's never opened the door, any door, before in his life, but we got in, in the end, and he asked me to sit down.'

'Did he seem embarrassed or nervous?'

'No. Not that I noticed. In fact, I can remember thinking, "What's he going to lumber me with now?" He asked me if I'd like a cup of coffee, though we'd both just had one. And then he put his stick away and sat down. "Helen, what I'm about to say now may come as a shock. Would you consent to become my wife?" Just like that. Not raising his voice. My skin prickled. "Consent". I felt odd, dizzy.' She laid her breathless sentences out for him, open, widely separate.

'What did you say?'

'Nothing for a bit. Nor did he. I suppose I thought, if what I was going through could be described as thought, he'd say why he'd proposed, but he didn't. We just sat there. Then I dragged my wits together, and thanked him, and said it was a surprise, and that I would want to think about it. He still didn't speak. You know how he slumps sideways on to his desk. I thanked him again. I said a formal thing, that I was honoured, and got up. I went across and kissed him on the forehead and still he didn't move. When I asked him if he was all right, he nodded, and mumbled. I let myself out.' She shook her head, to rid herself of confusion. 'My legs were trembling. I could hardly walk, I really shuddered.'

'Have you seen him today?'

'No. I don't usually come in. I've been back in Lincoln Hall.'

She strolled over to her chair, turned it to face him.

'I've just slipped in here. I wanted to see you before you went. I ought to have rung to make sure you'd be in. But I

64

don't know what I'm doing. I feel ill, Joe, weak, stupid. When I came out of his room, I was shaken, but I can understand that. It was as if he'd exposed himself. But now, I can't make head or tail of anything.'

'I take it as read that you don't want to accept the proposal?'

'I don't know that. I'm thirty-five, Joe. He's sixty-two. In three years he'll have retired.'

'And you'll have nearly thirty to finish.'

'Do you think I ought to take him?'

'Ought? What's that to the purpose?'

'He might need me. This accident. The boy killed. It may have shown him how vulnerable he is, all on his own. But we're both set in our ways. It might well prove a disaster.' She slapped the air with her left hand to dispel mosquitoes of doubt.

'Look here, Helly.' Harrington stopped. 'I'm in no position to give you advice. In some ways I'm as bad as he is. Eccentric bachelors.' He forced a laugh up from his lungs, nervously; she did not join him. 'I don't think very highly of him for a start. He's a lump of wet clay. No, let's be fair. He's not an out-and-out bastard. Just mischievous, when he can be bothered or is goaded beyond endurance. That's about it. He'll help you if he can do it without cost. You know I had an up-and-down with *The Times Higher Education Supplement*, but he wouldn't write to the editor on my behalf, though he knows him quite well. "These things are better left, Joe. You have right on your side, and in time people will come to see that." ' He did not imitate as accurately as Helen. 'He was clever once, but he isn't now. He's slow, and idle, doesn't read much, wastes his time and hasn't much conscience about it. I mean, what will he do when he retires? When there are no more committees? They'll drop him here quick enough, I tell you, because he'll be no use to them. Nor will he be asked to review anything or go anywhere to lecture. . . .'

'They've invited him to Princeton.'

'And what will he do when he gets there? A lot of harm to what reputation he's made. These young Americans'll run rings round him. And there he'll be ponderous, with his ancient wit, and his out-of-date scholarship. They'll piss all over him.'

'He's not so stupid as that, Joe.'

'You think not? Perhaps you're right.'

'Go on, Joe,' she ordered. 'I'm listening.'

'I'm trying to give you some idea of how he looks to me. Of course I see that's not much use to you.'

'I'm listening, Joe.' Her voice sounded like a tragedy queen's, hollow, barely human. She sat alongside her desk now, her fingers clasped above her knees, her face averted from him.

'Well. It's bloody hard, Helen, since I don't approve of him.'

'I want you to be frank.'

'He's an emotional cripple. You ought to know that better than I do. He's not half a man.'

'In what way?'

'Who or what does he like? Or love? Or applaud? Or support? When did he last show warmth? Who can say he pulled them out of a hole? How often does he give to charity? Who has he tried to understand? He's dead.'

She unclasped her fingers and rubbed the right hand along the polished wooden surround of her desk top, silently at first, then heavily.

'I didn't know you hated him so much, Joe.'

Harrington, holding his breath, blew it noisily out. 'Perhaps I exaggerate,' he answered. 'I can't claim to have made a close study of him.'

'But you're prepared to condemn him?'

'Yes. Given that it's the end of a tiring week, that I get carried away, I still can't find it in myself to praise him.'

She nodded, like a puppet.

'I'm sorry,' he said.

'No. I asked you to be frank.'

She continued to nod.

'I don't want you harming yourself. If you admired him it would be different. But you'll be tying yourself to an old man, who in three years' time will be nothing. Worse, he'll

66

know it. He'll have no secretaries or committees to occupy him. He won't want to read, or dig the garden, or listen to music. He'll want to cut a figure, and there'll only be you to see it. You'll run his errands, and type his letters, and sort out his bits and pieces. And it'll be at the expense of your work. He's selfish, that's the trouble. You'll be expected to drop everything if he gets a bit of a cold or a migraine or needs his shoes cleaning. It's not worth it, Helen. You've got this book to finish.'

'Who needs a book on Spenser?'

'It won't bring universal peace, or feed the Third World. No. But it's a small important attempt to describe human feeling and thinking that won't be done in the same way if you don't do it. And therefore it's not to be despised. Or lightly cast aside.' He grinned.

She filled her lungs.

'You've surprised me, Joe,' she said, after some time.

'Why is that?'

'You're more vehement than, than. . . .'

'Come, come. You didn't expect me to encourage you to marry him, did you?'

'No. I expected you to be dismissive of him, surely. But cold, and curt. "He's a fool and selfish with it." Something like that.' Harrington heard an echo of his own voice.

'I don't want you throwing yourself away.'

She stood up, collected three books, handling and rejecting from the piles at the top of the desk, consulting titles earnestly. She bit on the first finger of her left hand.

'Thanks, Joe.' She took the two steps to her high writing table, placed her books there, and stood as at a lectern, holding on to the sides, but staring out of the boring window. 'He's an old man, Joe. All his knowledge is tied up in little parcels. I told you he approved of student revolt in a mild way. Or so he says now. But if you ask him about it, whether it's the demos and sit-ins, or the theorists or practitioners, Marcuse, Régis Debray, Cohn-Bendit, he always comes out with the same little paragraph, like a tape. I'm not saying his views are stupid or wrong; they're sometimes quite witty, but they're always the same, not to be argued about. The words are fixed. You must have noticed, Joe.'

'Um. Yes. That's my impression when he's asked about, oh, let's say structuralism.'

'It's as if,' Helen sounded eager now, 'he feels he has to have a view because the V.C. or the registrar will expect it, and so he's put a few sentences together that will satisfy them, the intelligent and powerful outsiders. It's roused no interest in him, and it's not to be modified. It's a defence. And it's worse than ignorance. If he said he wasn't interested that would be enough, but, no, he comes out with his names, and his neat pack, and it's arrogant. "A professor is an ignorant man thinking." '

'Whitehead had done a bit on his own account.'

'What am I to do, Joe?' She switched topic, tone, position, now faced him.

'You haven't listed any of the advantages of marrying him.'

'Are there any?' She laughed now, but the laughter tailed away and her face became glum. 'I don't know. I sometimes think my literary training has unfitted me for life.'

'Heresy.' He pointed a finger at her. 'Tell you what. Come over to my place tomorrow afternoon. We'll have high tea. Cream shells and chocolate éclairs. And it puts decision-making off for another day.'

'I don't want to be a burden to you. You've plenty to occupy yourself with.'

'If you think it will do you any good. . . .'

'It will be just my luck to bump into him on the way out.' She buttoned her coat, shouldered her bag. 'Thanks, Joe, I will come. What time?'

8

In the night the weather turned colder, the wind from the northeast disturbing the twigs, blackening the sky.

Helen rang to say that her car had gone on the blink, and that meant she wouldn't arrive until after four-thirty. He offered to fetch her.

'No, thanks. It does me good to use the buses. What are you doing?'

'Clearing out the badger's lair.'

' "An image out of Spenser and the common tongue." '

Helen laughed; they enjoyed these peripheries of literature.

At three-thirty his door bell rang. He had finished his chores; the sky was becoming blacker, with snow cloud or night. Helen, he guessed, had misread the bus timetable. Anne Selby stood at the door.

'Am I disturbing you?' She looked frozen. 'Are you sure?'

He explained about Helen Southwell's visit, and led her inside.

'It's this manuscript of my dad's. He's coming round this afternoon, and I thought I'd collect it for him if it were convenient. We're all at home for tea. They've gone down to watch the Forest play this weekend, so they'll be fairly late. Traffic's very bad.'

Anne seemed uncomfortable. He provided instant coffee. She tapped the manuscript he had brought in.

'Is it any good?'

He explained what the memoir attempted, his own reservations, his guess that the account of life as a P.O.W. might be more interesting. He read her sentences, explaining why her father invariably seemed to miss out corroborative detail that would have livened the narrative.

'He's no good?' she asked.

69

'No. I wouldn't say that. He's not prepared to ditch his education. Stick to the subject. Be logical. No side-tracking. That's what he'd been told. So that it's clear; he knows what he wants to say but only inside these set limits. No streaks of the tulip.'

'For instance?' she pressed, troubled or puzzled.

'He won't talk about sex.'

'As a child?'

'As a child. Yes. Or any other time, I guess.'

She appeared affronted, blushed, a woman bunched, hunched over her cup.

'I find it pretty nearly impossible to give any view about my father's sex life,' she said stiffly.

'No. But I think any interest is likely to be in the trivia. Starching father's collars. What they ate for Sunday tea. What a house-meeting was like at a secondary school in the nineteen thirties. What prizes he won at Sunday school. When they first had a wireless, and what they listened to. Oh, pegging rugs from cut-up overcoats. You know the sort of thing.'

'He knows all about that.'

'But he won't touch it. No mention of outside lavatories. Or what they used for loo paper. No bedroom furniture described. No paper blinds.'

'I'll tell him.' She smiled almost radiantly. ' "The rough male kiss of blankets." ' He could not tell whether she made fun of him.

Anne packed away her father's manuscript, now in a stiff university foolscap envelope. She asked if there'd be any sense in her father coming up for a consultation. Harrington explained that he did not wish to direct Mr Reeves, or anyone else, on how to write, but, yes, he'd say his piece.

'He's a funny man. He doesn't take kindly to criticism.'

'Who *does?*'

'He's worse than most. You think I shouldn't talk like this about my own father, don't you? Whenever I see my mother, she always warns me about being too hard to him. I don't think it's likely. I don't like him. That's the top and bottom.

I ought to have grown out of it, but I haven't. We don't bother one another very much, but he's there.'

'And Tony?'

'He doesn't notice. Parents, his or mine, are a pain in the neck. No, a slight ache, or a crick.'

'You mean he doesn't realize how strong your dislike is?'

'He doesn't realize anything much.'

Under this pale, beautiful, strong exterior her father's sourness seethed. She demanded to be taken round the garden. When he instanced the cold, she ordered him to put an overcoat and scarf on.

'We'll look for signs of spring,' she said. 'There are plenty.'

The wind bit, but she was in no hurry. Against turned up, dark collar her cheeks demonstrated white health. She searched out snowdrops and crocus shoots, pointed to the bare beauty of trees, said she grew excited when it snowed. A few flakes whirled about in answer. They stood together, for no reason he could think of, inside the garden shed looking out through the uncleaned window. It seemed cosy in there, removed from the weather, dark, smelling of soil, the garden tools glinting in order on their wall.

Anne, hands deep in pockets, seemed near confession.

'We shall have to go in,' he told her. 'I have to light my dining room fire.' He explained again about Helen Southwell's visit, but Anne did not take the hint, watching him lay fire lighter, sticks, small coals. He put his match to it.

'Draws well, this chimney. Of course, I don't altogether approve of fire lighters.' A downdraught threw and withdrew a whirl of smoke into and from the room. 'That's the trouble with these old-fashioned affairs. Gas fires are infinitely more efficient. Heat the room up in no time. But it's one of the pleasures I can offer my visitors, an open fire.' He squared up the guard and she followed him out to the kitchen where he scrubbed his hands. 'I shall have a cassette of the Art of Fugue at the ready.'

'Lucky lady.'

They were watching the progress of the fire at twenty past four when Helen arrived. She laughed aloud to see both Joe

71

and Anne still in outdoor clothes. 'Has the central heating gone phut on you, then?'

The three stood together in the wide hall, in a clatter of talk, as at a reunion of very old friends. Harrington went out to fetch Anne more apples from his store, and returning – he'd had to empty a suitable box – found the two women happy. Helen was describing a bird she had seen that morning, pure white against the darkness of the sky; a gull, she thought, sheltering inland from the winter coast. He listened. Anne answered that this was a marvellous time of year; the two sounded elated, demonstrating a stagy excitement for each other. The women shook hands, in an ecstasy of smiling; Anne Selby took her box and envelope, glanced at her watch and within seconds had gone running for her bus.

Helen, helped off with her coat, asked no questions about Anne. When he offered a few sentences of information, she listened, but to his disappointment made only polite noises of acknowledgement. He led her to the dining room where they sat in front of the gas fire watching the teleprinter pumping out football results on television.

'Is that "nine" given as a figure and a word, because nobody expects a score of that size?' she wanted to know.

'Exactly.'

They glued their attention to the flickering screen.

'There's a twenty-five,' she said. 'And no letters.'

'That's rugby.'

'And big scores are the order of the day there?'

She knew quite well; both laughed as at a judge's assumed ignorance. They watched the football and racing results, took in the early evening news and switched off. Helen accompanied him into the sitting room where he mended the fire, drew his (rather, his sister's) red velvet curtains.

'We'll sit in here this evening.'

'I wonder if it's snowing.'

They lifted the end of a curtain but could make nothing out in the darkness. Helen had lost her earlier animation, and

72

seemed grateful to be invited into the kitchen to prepare the tea. She buttered the doughy white cobs.

'Cobs, baps, batches,' he said. 'Carbohydrate abounding. Bread's back in favour.'

'I eat wholemeal at home.'

'Wise woman. So do I. But today we'll be daft, accountable to nobody.' They laced their bread with both ham and tongue, and spread Branston pickle, laughing. When he produced his éclairs, his cream shells, Helen danced on the spot, like a child, beyond reason. Both ate slowly, swilled tea, considered and discussed the harm they did to their systems, then dismissed cholesterol, but chased its etymology up in the dictionary.

'Solid bile,' she reported.

'Same word as stereotype, stereoscope. I didn't know.'

'Solid.'

They washed up together and retired to the sitting room, where the fire, though flaming, had not yet heated the air. Harrington drew chairs nearer the hearth, wrapped Helen in a tartan blanket.

'I feel like an invalid.'

He knelt, mending his fire with careful building up of small coals.

'I'll be roasted.'

'In due course, yes. That's my intention.'

'This is a lovely room,' she said, content. 'Not like Paul's place.'

'I've only been in the room where he had the bed.'

'He must have bought the furniture when he first arrived. It's not very attractive.'

'And pictures?'

'Hardly any. And not nearly as many books as you'd expect.'

'Music centre? Didn't see one.'

'Yes. Quite a lot of Mozart. Piano concertos.'

'That puts him up a notch or two.'

'It looks shabby. Not dirty. Uncared for. Except for his bathroom. He'd just decorated that.'

'Himself?'

'Himself.'

They moved no nearer the serious, enjoyed *Stop the Week* on radio, arguing quite ferociously as they adjudicated on its strengths and weaknesses. All the time he worked at his fire, until he had driven his guest a yard further back from the hearth with the heat.

'It's very cosy here,' Helen admitted. 'Aren't I preventing you from working?'

'No. I rest on the seventh day. On well-established principle. A drink?'

He fooled about with glasses, tray, gin, tonic, the dash of vermouth, ice cubes. She sipped appreciatively, warily.

'I wish all my life was like this. Warm, comfortable, looked after.'

'Gin-sodden.'

She raised her glass ironically, not looking at him.

Not until ten minutes to nine – he glanced at the mantelpiece clock – did she speak about Wainwright and herself.

'I can't make my mind up.' Plaintively. 'It's no good.'

'The answer's "no", then. I should have thought that was obvious.'

'I feel sorry for him, Joe. He's finished.'

'That's not a good reason for saddling yourself with him. You don't admire him, do you?'

'He's written one good book. That's more than I shall.'

'Years ago. And it brought its advantages. Chair, status, decent salary. He's had his reward.'

'You despise him, don't you, Joe?'

'He's made a little go a long way. He buried his talents.'

'And did what instead?'

'Sucked up to the registrar, the vice chancellor, or both.'

Helen described the period when she stayed in his house, his fear, his babyish dependence, his complaints, even his prudishness. "Helen, I'm afraid my private parts are exposed to you again. I apologize." She had never been exactly sure whether he exaggerated his pain, his helplessness, or whether he assumed the rôle.

'What would he have done if you hadn't been there?'

'They'd have taken him back into hospital or convalescent home.'

'Did he get on well with the nurses?'

'Oh, yes. They loved him. He was a teddy bear. And a very good patient.'

'But not when you had him back home?'

'No. I didn't do it properly.' She displayed no rancour.

Together they summed up, supporting each other, trumping no aces.

'It looks as if I shall have to turn him down,' she said, in solemnity.

'That's what you want, isn't it?'

'To be a spinster?'

She recalled a man who had pursued her all through her undergraduate years in Oxford, and who now appeared, relaxed and handsome, on current affairs programmes on T V. 'He used to propose and threaten to commit suicide if I didn't accpept him.'

'And you.'

'I refused at first. Politely. I thought he was feeble. Then I accepted him, and backed out. And he's so dishy now.'

'And married?'

'I expect so.'

When he offered a third gin, she declined, asking for coffee. They went out together and opened the front door to check on the weather. Snow held off; a cloud-bound star or two twinkled; it struck very cold.

'You get back and keep the fire warm,' he ordered.

They drank coffee, and dissected the character of Jack Clough, who was enthusiastic about Helen's chapters on Spenser. 'He'll propose illegally next,' Harrington prophesied, pouring. Clough, married to a beautiful woman, affected cloth caps and carpentry. 'He's better than Paul.' They discussed the proposition sunnily, glad of the heaped-up fire.

At eleven she said she must go.

'What's the hurry?'

'I don't want to go at all.'

'What's that mean?'

'Oh, nothing.'

'It must be.'

'Paul will ring tonight or tomorrow morning.'

'The visitor's bed is made up. I could turn the radiator on.'

'That's asking too much, Joe. I mustn't make work for you. Or run away.'

'I'll put it on now.'

She made, to his surprise, no attempt to stop him. When he returned she asked at what time he usually went upstairs. He shook his head.

'Varies. Are you tired, then?'

'I didn't sleep well last night.'

'I've put an old pair of pyjamas in for you. You'll need to roll 'em up. Nurse the fire for a minute while I make the house safe.'

She crouched by the hearth, face forward, reddened, in cupped hands.

'Upstairs, then, madam.' Harrington was back.

Helen stood, threw her arms about his neck. Her mouth closed, openly, wetly, on to his. Surprised he pulled her into him, caressed her back, her buttocks, with overt but gentle sexuality. Her eyelids, blue-shaded, remained shut. He stroked her hair, now beginning to escape its customary neatness. She clung the tighter, impressively strong for one of her size. Edging her backwards he laid her across the settee, settling her head into a cushion, stroking the small, handsome breasts. As he broke roughly from a kiss, he saw her eyes wide open, summing him up, judging. He knelt on the floor.

'No,' she whispered. 'No.'

'No, what?'

Helen sat up, pulled down her skirt, swung her legs to the edge of the settee, which dwarfed her.

'It's you I love,' she answered. She stroked her forehead, ridding herself of illusion. 'You knew that, didn't you?'

He knelt, mum.

'You knew, Joe. You must have known.'

Harrington could not bring himself to utter. She hutched along the settee, lowered her feet to the floor, made sure her shoes were firmly on, scrabbled again at her face.

'I didn't know,' he said, finally, weakly.

'Paul does. He keeps asking me why I. . . .' She dashed the rest of the sentence aside with her left hand. 'You don't love me?'

'Not in the way you mean.'

'Not in any way.' She dismissed his rider, authoritatively, unemphatically, as she might fault a student's poor attempt at elucidation. 'That's how it is, Joe.' Her eyes brimmed, but could not overflow. Neither man nor woman moved, he kneeling, she neat, small-breasted, on the very edge of the settee.

'I'm sorry,' he offered, at length.

'It's not your fault. It can't be.'

He laid his face into the velvet of the settee cushions. Faintly her perfume touched his senses. For some minutes he crouched there, unable to push himself to his feet, lust as yet uncontained, conscience giddy.

'We're a mess,' she said soberly. The word steadied him.

'I'm a bastard.' He stumbled upwards. 'I ought to have known. I'm sorry, Helen.' She reached out, touched his forearm briefly. 'It's this bloody marriage of mine. It did for me.'

Now tears splashed silently down her face which preserved serenity, an undistorted plainness. Upstairs, last thing, he asked, 'Will you be all right?'

Her face shone wetly.

'Yes. Don't you worry.'

'Would you like a cup of tea in bed in the morning? Or coffee?'

For all the response he might have been speaking a foreign tongue. She smiled socially, made for the bathroom where he had put out a new brush and toothpaste. A swagger of her shoulders did nothing to reassure him. He heard the splashing of water, the returning footsteps, saw to the extinguishing of lights, but could not sleep.

77

9

Early in February Harrington received a letter from Paulina.

She apologised, at odd length, for her silence, thanked him for his Christmas card, and proposed calling in on him again. She named the date, a Saturday, one week ahead. Edmond had been ill, was still off colour, and she had been busy beyond all reason with television schedules. Now she was due in Manchester for a recording and would call in on him, if it interrupted nothing. He wondered if she had deliberately made it easy to excuse himself. He rang the London address, left a message of acceptance with some female who did not identify herself.

Helen Southwell tiptoed in and out of their room at university. They were friendly; she modestly grumbled that progress on her book had again come to a halt. It took her a week to mutter offendedly that she had refused Paul, and that he had taken it stoically.

'He said an odd thing,' she whispered, standing, one hand on the door handle, an arm full of books.

'What was that, then?'

'He asked if he could; no, he. . . . Would it upset me if he asked me out for a drink now and then. "I know what you're going to say, Helen",' she mimicked admirably. ' "That as long as I don't read into your acceptance any kind of hope or promise." ' He had bunched his fists in his trousers' pockets, she recalled. "I think I shall love no one else, but I think you know that." She edged the door open. 'I felt like crying. I did. I ran into the stockroom.'

She slipped out. Was this a parallel, a parable?

Harrington tried to imagine the professor mouthing these reported sentences, which veered well out of character. They had the ring of a film script, poor but possible. But Helen

78

would have remembered accurately. When awkward men attempt to verbalize unusual depth of feeling, the result is flat, laughable, but at least Wainwright had not disguised his confusion with quotation. 'I think I shall love no one else.' What did that emotional cripple mean by 'love'?

Anne's husband had slipped on his front-garden path early in January, broken his ankle, and needed to be ferried to and from his library. A poor patient, his wife reported, he groaned himself out of his family's sympathy. Father Reeves threatened to descend on Harrington for advice or polemics, but never appeared. The weather grew duller, colder, with unpleasant periods of sleet. The daily trundle through tutorials, lectures, marking and setting seemed almost pleasant, a cushion against the grey chill.

On the Saturday morning of Paulina's visit a secretary from the B.B.C. in Manchester rang to say Miss Street hoped to arrive soon after three-thirty, though she could not be quite sure. Uncertain how well fed Paulina would be, he cooked up a large casserole of beef. Plain hot fare this winter day for her. Nevertheless, he rushed from room to room squaring up, moving objects, cleaning windows that would be curtained almost as soon as she arrived.

She had not come by six o'clock, nor had messages of excuse.

By seven he had given her up; at twenty-two minutes past she rang his door bell.

'Am I welcome?' She then relapsed into silence, making no attempt to be sociable. She flopped in front of the gas fire, asked for a big whisky, said she's be glad to eat if it was no trouble.

'Half an hour?'

'I'm in no position to be laying down conditions.'

Though she said she was worn out, she did not appear so. Her skin was fresh, eyes wide, unbaggy. She wore wide maroon trousers and a hillbilly blouse.

'That's done me good,' she said, putting down the empty glass.

'Help yourself to more.' She did so.

79

Harrington kept himself busy in the kitchen, appearing from time to time at the door to ask about her comfort. Again he was surprised at the physical effect of her presence on him, as she explained the reason for her lateness, a detour into Cheshire to make a short introductory recording near the home of the producer of her *Much Ado*. They had used an Elizabethan manor house, and the producer's four children, so that Beatrice was seen as Madam Benedick, with her family. The whole would not last above one and a half minutes, would in all probability never be shown at all, but such were the mores of the medium that this time and money had to be invested. She spoke with cheerful nonchalance; the producer, Francis Foulkes, was good, wanted to record *Uncle Vanya* with her and Paul Scofield inside the next three months. 'Made the waiting about worth it.' She had tried – she offered the information late – to ring about three, but no one had answered. He guessed that he had been at the end of his garden, on his one trip to the compost heap. She laughed, suspiciously, he thought.

She daintily ate her way through a helping and a half of the casserole, saying she had nibbled only in the past three days.

'I use these one-off trips as slimming periods. Especially this, because I knew you'd have something delicious and wholesome.'

He inquired about her husband's health.

'He's much better. I'm sure of that, but he complains, and that makes it difficult to know how we stand. He has no standards to judge by. He's been pretty healthy all his life, and I think he gets frightened. I tell him he works too hard.'

At the end of the meal, after she had drained her third glass of whisky (she had refused wine), she asked bluntly if she could stay overnight. 'I've done enough driving for one day.' He made her a bed up, and she telephoned her husband. As far as he made out – her voice rang clear and he listened carefully – she did not say where she was spending the night.

He insisted that she sat while he washed the dishes. She

poured herself another glass of whisky, pointing out she would soon be drunk.

'Is that good or bad?' He had difficulty making sense. There were few signs of it.

'I'm glad I rang Edmond while I was still coherent.'

'Was he expecting you back?'

'He wasn't put out. He knows how schedules are shifted about, and how accommodating I am.' She laughed. Settled later in front of the fire, legs at full stretch, she commented, 'This is cosy. And unusual for me. You don't know how pleasant it is to have the evenings to yourself, no theatre, nobody to entertain, no telephone calls.' She seemed content almost to drowse, to shut her eyes to the world, but she would then liven herself to ask him a question. 'What time do you go to bed?' or 'How do you like it up here?' or to state, 'You look well, Joe. It must suit you.' The questions sounded friendly.

'In this dump?' He felt the need to rile her.

'I didn't say that. It wouldn't do for me. Too far off the beaten track. You need to be to hand in my profession.'

Later still on her fifth glass of whisky, she said, with a sober, sombre emphasis, 'I've been worried about you, Joe. Not about you in yourself, if you know what I mean. You're a survivor, for all your ups and downs. It's between you and me, I mean.'

He made noises of concerned interest. She cocked a suspicious eye.

'You seemed last time to look on me as the enemy. Of course, it may be my misreading of the situation. Edmond didn't notice anything. Or so he said, but perhaps he didn't want to start an argument. He's like you. Peace at any price, at least in public. But it's so, isn't it? You hate me somehow, don't want anything to do with me.'

'I'm doing my best for you now.' He'd keep it light.

'I want to be friends,' she argued.

'Why? Or alternatively, why not?'

'That three years we were married meant something, means something to me. We shared some good times, didn't we?'

'I don't disagree.'

'But it had to come to an end. It was already breaking up. You were going to move here, and you couldn't expect me to come with you, that was for certain. We'd have been parted a great deal of the time, and fighting when we were together. It wouldn't have worked, would it? You must admit that.'

'Marriages have survived on less.'

'No, they haven't. Not anything I could call a marriage. You didn't really need me. You're a tough. It would have petered out, anyway. So it was better to finish it as it did.'

' "Shot? So quick, so clean an ending." '

She ignored the quotation.

'You'd have liked to have clung on to your bits and pieces, I don't doubt. But they would not have constituted a marriage.'

'Look, Pauly,' he had not often used the diminutive even in the years of marriage, did not think of her as such. 'You preferred someone else. Rightly perhaps. He could offer you more than I could. But that's the top and bottom of it.'

'I don't think that's anything like the truth.'

'And you said so, plainly. Out of the blue. "I love somebody else." Simple as that. I don't blame you, in the sense that you weren't coming up with the truth. You were saying exactly what you felt at that time. You made no attempt to fight against it.'

'How can you say that?'

'Oh, come on, now. Be honest with yourself, at least.'

'You're beginning to be angry, Joe. Again.'

'Let's drop it, then.'

'No. I'd like to sort this out if it's possible.'

'Why?'

'Because,' she spoke slowly, words unslurred, 'I want you to know how I felt about it. But you're hurt still, and suspicious of me. We could be friends.'

'If someone hit me over the head with an iron bar for no very good reason, I'd certainly look on his next appearance with suspicion. Yes.' Harrington kept it near-jovial. 'But if you can offer some rational explanation. . . .'

'Our marriage had run its course, Joe. Its useful life was over.'

'Not as far as I was concerned.'

'It takes two to make a marriage.'

'Thank you.'

'The same old awkwardness.'

'I don't want to argue with you,' Harrington answered placidly enough. 'But since you insist, let's get the facts straight. You wanted to marry someone else, and you said so, regardless of any consideration of my feelings.'

'Because we could not go any further.'

'Because you wanted me out of the way, so you could take on Edmond. You said as much. I'll give you that.'

'It's not true, Joe.'

'That's why our marriage was broken. You wanted to marry someone else.'

'If you think back, you'll remember that I told you I couldn't go out of London with you, that something had radically changed in our relationship.'

'It had that.'

'Don't choose to misunderstand me. You must remember that I said that we were beginning to quarrel, to nag. . . . You don't deny it, do you?'

'That I remember? Or that we nagged?'

'Don't dodge, Joe.'

He did not speak, fought down spleen, opened the whisky, poured himself another finger, then waved the bottle in her direction. She smiled brilliantly, held out the glass.

'I can't understand,' he began, 'why you have to bring all this up. I'm glad to do you a good turn, if I can. But our marriage went bust, for whatever reasons, and I don't hold myself spotless and blameless, but if every time we meet we hold another inquest, then I must call a halt.'

'Don't you ever ask yourself why I do it?'

'Yes. And come up with unacceptable answers.'

'Such as?' She seemed to expand with pleasure. Even in his ill temper he recalled the hymn: 'And every bosom swell/With pure seraphic joy.' He giggled, but answered,

'Malice.'

'You mean I get pleasure from opening old wounds?' He answered her cliché with a courteous, sarcastic bow. 'Couldn't it as easily be guilt?'

'Or curiosity.'

'Or temperament. I say what I think. I didn't notice any objection when I said we ought to get married.'

'There's a difference.' Harrington was mild.

'Don't think I don't know. But we'll drop it if that's what you want. I'm sorry. I really am. I just felt I owed it to you, to offer some, some sort of explanation. You don't see it like that.' She nodded, rather drunkenly now. 'I owe you a great deal, since I've used that word.' There was nothing inebriated about her; her voice, without additional volume, took on power, a vibration not to be ignored on the back row of the gods. 'That two-three years when we were married sorted me out. I think you realize that. I was a mess when we first came across each other. You bailed me out; no, helped me find myself, and I shall be eternally grateful. It didn't last. . . .'

'The devil howling "Ho".'

She twisted her lips sourly.

'That was a pity perhaps,' she continued. 'But it was a fact of life. You might look on marriage differently from me. As an absolute. Till death do us part. I don't. I can't. But I just can't believe that the end came as a surprise to you.'

He nodded, as if conceding her point, and avoided her eyes. She waited, and was received in silence. No answer would be given; he'd let her talk herself out. She continued, but without breaking new ground: he had done her good; she was grateful; their marriage had no further life in it.

Strangely, he could barely believe it himself, he did not mind her persistence now. When she had married him she was on the verge of large success, though she did not know it. During those three years she had become a household name, whose opinions were canvassed on radio and television about literature, current programmes, cookery. She appeared in panel games, where she demonstrated a sweet sharpness, a quickness of wit never indulged in at another's expense.

She read a great deal to keep up with her husband's work, and with a retentive memory could clip out an apt, often unusual quotation. Paulina Street was alive, unforgettable, no mere pretty nonentity.

Harrington remembered how soon he had discovered her cleverness, from her interests, from the speed she mastered a new topic, or raised pertinent objections to his theses, or drew out in no time the interests of his colleagues at U.C.L. with inquisitorial efficient charm. As she questioned, she made some dull don feel important. This beautiful woman, whom every man if not woman in the room wanted to talk to, listened and learnt from one's lips, like a star pupil. It seemed a kind of miracle. It altered pedagogics.

Of course she could be harsh in judgement. On their return to the flat she would dismiss as slow, a favourite word, or bogus, some man she had sent home entranced. And these judgements more often than not were right. She learnt quickly, profited from her husband's expertise, picked up some of his studious habits, but in public, competitive as she was, never bitchily scored off others. Those first months of marriage became marvellous; the two stimulated each other so that even periods of necessary absence, at the theatre, at recordings, conferences became part of the brilliance of living. Sexual charge imbued every exchange. They were angels, messengers of some high, pagan god.

Now he smiled wrily.

Paulina, explaining herself, was no longer the bright, acute conversationalist; she had become a great lady, an aristocrat sufficiently sure of her status, her *gravitas*, to be able to offer apologies to lesser mortals without loss of face, even with enhancement of her own superiority. Honesty was all. She did not talk down to him. It was he who realized he occupied an inferior place, and marvelled that she could bring herself to address him as an equal. As his academic friends had been bowled over by the intelligence of this beautiful woman, he was now to be captured, overwhelmed by her humility.

Harrington, unsure of his opinions, waited. She finished her whisky, refused more, kissed him on the cheek, went to bed. He slept badly, rose soon after eight, breakfasted with the Sunday papers, dawdled. About ten he heard her running the bath; by ten-thirty she appeared, dressed differently from the evening before, her face carefully made up. She took cereal and coffee, politely, but without talk, as if she laboured under disappointment. He hovered; she at his insistence propped *The Observer* in front of her at the table, but never turned from the first page. When she rose she asked if she could telephone her husband; that was short-lasting, business-like, an inquiry after Edmond's health and an announcement of arrival time. Neither participant lingered. Paulina disappeared upstairs, returning after ten minutes, dressed in her driving coat and carrying her bags.

'Thank you for having me.' Harrington dried his hands; he was scraping potatoes. He carried her luggage to the car.

'Shall we see each other again?' he asked.

'Possibly. Many thanks. I'm glad to have been here.'

She wound up her window, raised a gloved hand and was gone.

Later in the day when Thomas Reeves rang up about his memoir Harrington briefly listened, said he was too busy at present to see the man. He was surprised at his own sour tone. He had expected something from this visit of Paulina and it had not materialized. He tried to dismiss his foolishness, and failed.

10

At eight that same Sunday night Anne Selby thumped his back door. The noise startled him; visitors should use the front bell. He had reached the last paragraph of a long review of an anthology of eighteenth-century verse, knew exactly what he wanted to say, even to the words, but wrote slowly in hope of some last-minute improvement, some sharp turn of phrase that experience led him to expect. He parked Anne in front of the fire while he completed the final half-dozen lines, without benefit of inspirations.

'Don't you work in your study?' she asked as he finished.

'Not always. When it's cold, I don't see the sense of heating two rooms.'

He put his review away, looking forward to rereading it the next day. She had sat peaceably with her hands in her lap during the ten minutes it took him to complete the work. He tucked his papers with ostentation into a folder, then rubbed his hands.

'Now then. A drink? Cup of coffee?'

Harrington looked her straight in the face for the first time; her features were strained, stretched, taut.

'Are you all right?'

'I've walked out of the house.'

The harmless sentence reeked of venom. She delivered it with teeth clamped.

'You've left the boys?'

'All of them. I can only stand so much.'

At his repeated, prosaic question she chose coffee. On his return she had not moved an inch.

'I carry Tony round like a baby. And he never thinks to thank me. I know he's in pain. But I'd got Billy ready for bed; he came down in his pyjamas, and Tony sat with his foot up dabbing at his computer. It was too much. He'd complained that afternoon about the lunch. Stodgy, he said. I'd argued back, and he'd looked so hurt. Could I get him the indigestion tablets? I could have kicked him. And there he perched, making no attempt to talk to the boys or entertain them or anything else. I carry the whole burden of the house.'

'What did you say?'

'Nothing. I took my coat, scarf and bag and walked out.'

'Did they hear you? Do they realize you've gone?'

'I don't know. They'll find out soon enough.'

'Where did you intend to go? To your father's?'

'I didn't think. I just had to burst out of the place before I went mad.' She seemed easier each time she spoke.

'Will you go back tonight?' Now she looked at him as if she found the question unfair, obscene.

'I don't know. I just want them to find out that I'm not at their beck and call every minute of the day.'

'I see. Drink your coffee.'

Though she picked up her cup she did not follow his instruction, but gabbled into complaint. Tony's lack of thought, his immersion in his computers and library, his failure to thank her, his neglect of the boys, his illness, surliness, taciturnity, his untidiness. As anecdote tumbled into anecdote her voice grew shriller, her delivery more rapid. Finally, at some triviality about a coupon from a newspaper she had asked him to post and which she had found a week later in a coat pocket while she searched for handkerchieves to wash, her voice broke, her face collapsed round the screwed eyes as she sobbed. Harrington watched; she had abandoned herself to her grief, crouping, screeching, snuffling by turn, rocking backwards and forwards like a Middle Eastern mourner. Though her behaviour had something of the formality of a performance about it, he could not tell whether she was aware of him. She seemed possessed; the tear-streaked flesh, blubbery, was transmogrified; the mouth a twisting, gaping caricature. He waited for her to calm herself; it seemed not to happen. When the crying subsided, she sat gripped, but almost immediately a further hiccough of temper, sorrow or frustration racked the body which became noisy again, and mobile. The bout lasted for a quarter of an hour, while he looked on. He did not touch her, mutter consolation, even get out of the way. Time passed leadenly slow, but he did not interefere. At last, when she seemed stiller, signalling this by turning her face away from him, he stood, picked up her coffee cup.

'Would you like a sip?' His question seemed itself twisted, pitched between the prosaic and the facetious. She took the coffee from him but her hands trembled with such violence that the cup rattled comically in the saucer. She managed to touch her lips with the rim. He could not tell whether or not she drank.

'Is it cold?'

She did not answer, shrank inside herself as she returned cup and saucer to the table.

'I'll make a fresh one. You go up to the bathroom and swill your face.'

When she did not budge, he put a hand under her arm and obediently she rose. He led her outside to the hall, directed her to the bathroom, watching her progress upstairs. She took two steps and paused, left hand on banister to retain balance, three more and a further pause, then a stagger to the top where she dithered. Not once did she look back; she moved like one immersed in her own helplessness.

'Straight on. Third door,' he shouted.

Anne Selby came down after ten minutes, calmer but on the edge of violent change. He placed a small hot cup of sweetened coffee by her chair. Her face had not lost its rubbery lack of definite shape. Hands fluttered; she had done nothing about her hair. She took her coffee, sipped gratefully.

'You've put sugar in.' The voice, feeble enough, was controlled.

'You need it. Would you like a soupçon of whisky?'

She shook her head, gingerly smiling, fleetingly.

'Another?' he asked, when she had drained her cup. She frowned as if the question were too hard to answer. 'That must mean "yes",' he ventured, making for the kitchen.

'What time is it?' she asked, reaching for the new cup.

'Five minutes past nine.'

'Is that all? What time did I come?'

'Eight. Eight-fifteen or thereabouts.'

Harrington thought, unwounded, how he had kept her sitting while he polished off the tempered blame and praise of his review. The compiler of the anthology had sought out, unusually, women writers, feminine views, while he, milord Harrington, sitting in judgement had not noticed Anne's distress, as he concentrated on the weight and balance of his concluding sentences. She had been still, untroubled, or so he had thought. Not until he had questioned her, or she had answered, had she broken down. That quietness in the chair while he had concluded his unimportant words had contained her worst moments of trial, the social hiding of lacerating emotion, while he had passed by on the other side in donnish unconcern.

She had demonstrated the strength of her feeling by the duration of her crying jag. That fifteen minutes had stretched interminably; he could barely credit that her body had persisted so long in such fury of behaviour.

He looked at the now composed figure, the swollen red eyes.

'How do you feel?' he asked, without emphasis.

'As if I've been beaten up.'

He considered, then spoke in spite of himself.

'Have you ever . . . ?' He stopped himself.

'Been beaten up? No.' The voice struck brighter, almost cheerfully. 'But I can imagine.'

They sat in silence, tinkering with their coffee, in embarrassment on his side. Now and then she sniffed, single vigorous sounds. The mantelpiece clock ticked with monumental, boring gravity.

'What are you going to do?' He risked the question.

'Don't ask me. I feel as if I shall fall into pieces if anything bothers me.' She looked up, almost as if to check she had not exceeded propriety. 'I'm sorry.'

Again a period of no speaking increased his awkwardness.

There ought, he considered, to be some word or gesture to begin an alteration of healing. He failed to discover either. Anne found her voice first.

'I shall have to be getting back.'

'I'll drive you over.'

'That means getting your car out.'

'I don't want you walking through the dark streets at this hour of night. You just take your time and collect yourself.'

'Tony will be angry.' Her voice was steady now. 'Especially when he finds out where I've been. He'll say I've been broadcasting his faults. He wants to impress you. He was delighted when you rang him at the library about a word processor. We had nothing else for days. Have you got it?'

'Yes. My Christmas present to myself.'

'And did you follow his advice?'

'I did.'

'And is it successful?'

'Very.'

'You weren't using it tonight.'

'No. Atavism broke in, or out. That was the first time for weeks I'd taken to my biro.'

They laughed, tentatively.

'Does my face look a mess?' she asked. 'Be honest.'

'I can see you've been crying.'

'You mean he'll know? And my hair?'

'Could do with the comb, yes.'

Anne asked permission to repair her outward faults. Though her hair was smoothly brushed upwards when she returned, her swollen eyes still wrecked her appearance. In the car she looked small, spoke little. To make conversation he asked about her father's memoir.

'He doesn't like criticism,' she answered. 'Like me.'

'Tell him to phone if he wants to talk about it. I was a bit short with him last time. Or if he wants me to read any more he's written.'

'I will.'

She crouched quietly, silent until they arrived.

91

'I must apologise. Again.' Anne released her seat belt. 'Now I've got to think what to say to them. What time is it?'

'Ten past ten. It's not late. The pubs aren't closed.'

'Thank you.'

'Let me know how . . . things turn out, are.'

She waved a hand, walked quickly up the front path, letting herself in. Satisfied she was not bolted out, he drove off.

Harrington had no sooner entered the front door than his telephone rang. Surprised, for he did not encourage callers after ten, he picked up the yellow instrument, heard the voice of his professor.

'Is that you, Joe?' Reassured, Wainwright did not immediately continue, but puffed with regularity into the mouth-piece. The soft, magnified sound might be construed as a message. Then with a long indrawing of breath he began, 'I'm sorry to trouble you at this time of night. I suppose it could have waited until tomorrow. Yes, I imagine so.' Again the deep intake, this time through the nostrils. 'It's about Helen. Helen Southwell. I should like to talk to you about her. If you have no objection, that is.' The telephone magnified Professor Wainwright's embarrassment. 'But not over the telephone, I think. Can we meet somewhere? Conveniently?' The words separated themselves one from the next.

'Where do you suggest?'

'Perhaps at your home.' No hesitation about that.

'Right. When?'

'Well, not tonight, I think. Though I'm quite willing to turn out, if that seems best, to, to you.' Harrington scotched the idea. 'I'm worried about Helen, Joe. And you're the person I should consult. I think very highly of that girl.'

'We all do.'

The professor did not answer, as if rebuffed. Then aloud he consulted his diary, and between them, businesslike, they fixed their meeting at nine on the next Friday evening.

'I don't want to interrupt your work. Or take up your free evenings.'

'That will suit me.' Harrington sounded grim, yielding

92

nothing. Wainwright practised his breathing routine, softly uttered thanks. Harrington jammed the phone down.

Next morning at the university he reported Wainwright's approach to Helen, but she, on her way to an early lecture, said that she and the professor had barely exchanged twenty words in the last week, that she guessed the man was lonely, and that it told on him at ten-thirty on a Sunday night. As far as she was concerned, no crisis had arisen.

'Is he going to blame me?' Harrington asked, leafing through letters.

'For what?'

'For your turning him down.'

Her expression twisted itself into amusement; she reached for the door handle, her face brightly towards him.

'You may have something there.'

She was gone; the door was shut. He began to read, making notes.

That evening, Tom Reeves, Anne's father, rang about his typescript. He began reasonably enough, but as Harrington advanced tentative criticisms Reeves sounded angrier, and in the end bluntly accused the other man of encouraging the writing of pornography. 'It's all you university people are interested in: putting stuff in such fancy ways nobody wants to read it, or coming down in favour of sexual filth. Now I'm telling you there's more to life than pulling a woman's knickers off. As some of you educated perverts ought to know.' The voice shouted hotter and Reeves suddenly, having completed a sentence, banged the telephone into its cradle.

Harrington, intrigued but untroubled, continued with his reading. He was almost ready to write the short book on Yeats: if he had a chapter or two stored on the word processor before Easter he might easily have the first draft complete and the new book started before the summer vacation ended. His progress pleased him; he had done a very substantial amount of preparation in spite of or perhaps because of inter-ruptions, but he knew himself well enough to realize that a completed draft would find him changing his mind. This book must be short; his publishers continued to remind him

that he was writing a primer, an introductory study for 'A'
level candidates or first year university students, but he was
determined to make of it something his colleagues would not
despise. His failure to master Wallace Stevens rankled; he'd
make that good before he was done.

Tony Selby rang one lunch time from his office.

'I wanted to get in touch before, but this ankle hobbles me
still. I wanted a word about Anne, but I'm dependent upon
her for transport, so that won't do. But many thanks for
looking after her the other night.'

'Is she all right?'

'Well, the fact that I'm immobilized means a lot more
responsibility for her, and I suppose I am not always cheerful.
She has to ferry me to work, and to the outpatients' department, as well as seeing to the kids. It gets topside of her.'

'I see.'

'I'd like to talk to you about it, but not over the phone.
When I can get about under my own steam. Of course she
may be on an even keel by then. But thanks for all you did.
Can I send her round to see you from time to time? She rates
your advice highly, if that's the phrase.'

Selby rang off, gruffly, confidently, handing out last
compliments.

Harrington classifed the man as impatient because this was
the second time he had rung confidentially about his wife,
and then refused to say anything. Perhaps inquisitive ears
sprouted all over the public library, tuned in for snatches of
scandal. If so, a sensible man would not take the risk.

At least three times in the week Harrington met Paul Wainwright in the university, but on no occasion did either raise the
topic of Helen Southwell or the professor's visit. Wainwright
seemed his glum self, grousing about the weather or the
infighting for funds. He asked about Yeats and was told for
the second time about the projected book on Romanticism.

'You're the best man in the country to do that, as I told
Tom Templar.'

'I'm surprised he takes an interest in such low budget
projects.'

'It could sell well, and for a long time, if you do it properly.' He coughed his chest clear. 'As you will.'

So he'd received the invitation because Wainwright had recommended him. A sobering thought, if the truth. On the Friday night Joe Harrington set his work out so that he could spend the whole of Saturday and Sunday on his Yeats book. The professor arrived ten minutes late, puffing apologies, not having realized how far out it was, and having been once misdirected. Joe offered him alcohol, but this was refused. 'Since the accident I do not drink when I have to drive.' He smiled, and answered questions about his recovery with easy familiarity, even drawing up his trouser leg to display scars. He suggested black coffee – he watched his weight; congratulated Joe on his house, saying his own was like a nomad's tent. 'I've had twenty-three years in it, but it doesn't show. I'm a sojourner in a strange land.'

Wainwright sipped at his boiling coffee as soon as it was presented, put it shakily down, and began.

'I don't want to waste your time, Joe. But I'd appreciate a confidential word. About Helen. I'm glad you found it in your way to accommodate me here. We shan't be interrupted as we should in my room.' He looked about. For eavesdroppers? Harrington pitied the man's uncertainty.

'Now. Helen Southwell. I think I should make something plain. You may or may not know that I proposed marriage to her, to Dr Southwell. I suppose you'd heard that?'

Harrington stared at the wall over Wainwright's head, as if the news had banged him into dumbness. He did not reply, though Paul obviously waited for an answer.

'She refused me. That is not surprising in view of the disparity in our ages. But it came as a great disappointment to me. To you, Joe, I must seem a mammoth, a pachyderm quite out of date. Too ancient to feel. Now, that is not the case. As far as emotion is concerned I am not so very different from the young man I was at seventeen. Thin-skinned, alert for insult, uncertain, delicate, unbalanced; everything I appear to you not to be. You understand that?'

95

Harrington nodded, gravely. Certainly he felt surprise at Wainwright's choice of words.

'When they sent me home after my accident, Helen Southwell of her own volition moved in with me, looked after me. That girl returned me to life. She cared for my most intimate bodily needs but I need say no more about that. She, and I use biblical language advisedly, restored my soul. I had killed a child. Oh, everyone assures me it wasn't my fault, but that makes no difference. I was lost, damned below Judas in my own mind. Added to this was considerable pain, and inconvenience, from which I am still not free. Helen Southwell,' the constant use of both names seemed to add sincerity, 'came and little by little lifted me from my desperation, made me capable again of life. You see what I'm driving at?'

Harrington did not answer, but felt the more boorish for his silence.

'I owe her an enormous debt which I am expressing badly, baldly to you. I am not even sure if I am making a great fool of myself in your eyes. But I do not mind that. It's beside the point. She did me a great service, which I can in no shape or form repay. Moreover, and here I misled myself, deluded myself, I became convinced that she thought more of me, more, that is, than of a valued colleague.' He looked up, writhing, at his junior.

'Did she say as much?' Harrington blurted out.

'That is difficult to answer. Yes and no. In my pain and agitation I was in no position to make stringent judgements. She said words of endearment, yes. She touched and caressed me, yes. There was no sexual exchange, if that's what you mean.' He lifted a dull, accusatory face, dead-eyed. 'I had thought very highly of that young woman, as a scholar and as a teacher. Now she was a human being of a different category.'

Professor Wainwright spoke breathily, struggling like a mystic to find words expressive of, adequate to his experience. What Harrington feared was an accusation that he was responsible for Helen's behaviour.

96

'I understand this, Paul,' he answered, gently enough, 'or how you feel about it. It's bad. But why are you telling me?'

'Because of Helen. Look. You share a room with her. For all I know, you share confidences with her as no other member of the department does. You have influence over her.' His voice quickened. 'She looks on you as successful. You work. You get things published, and they are well-regarded. You don't neglect your students, but that does not impede your own progress. You've got, as they say, your act together. In a way none of the rest of us has. That first book of yours, oh, on the pre-Romantics, oh, I'll forget my own name one of these days, this nominal aphasia,' Harrington did not help him out, 'will last. Students will still be referring to it long after you have retired from the academic scene, long after you would wish them not to do so. One of the ironies of continuing to think. We, Jack Clough, Harold Morris for all his sourness, Harry Spellman, I, the lot of us would all nominate you as the successful man of the department.'

'It doesn't feel like that.'

'That may be so. That may be the very essence of your success. But.' He held up a hand to forestall an interruption Harrington did not intend to make. His behaviour seemed extraordinary, quite unlike that towards his friends the registrar or the dean of sciences. Helen's theory of prepared packages of knowledge to be handed out as acceptable offerings gathered weight; the professor's asking for help in an exotic field explained his outlandish, clumsy approach. 'But. You are so regarded. By Dr Southwell, especially. That's why I suggested she move in with you.'

'I see.'

'Has she given you any reason why she could not find it possible to look on me as a prospective husband?'

'No.'

'You did know I had proposed?'

'I did.'

'From Helen?'

'Who else? I don't suppose either of you broadcast it.'

'But she told you?'

'I said so.'

At the sharp tone of the reply Wainwright picked up his coffee as if to defend his face. He held the saucer awkwardly in front of his paunch.

'She did not do so as a matter of ridicule?'

'No. She took it perfectly seriously. As you'd expect with her.' Harrington snatched a breath through his mouth. 'Look, Paul, any discussion between Helen and myself is confidential. You can take it from me that she didn't regard your proposal as a subject for mockery. I think she told you at the time that she was honoured. I see no reason to disbelieve that. More I am not prepared to say.'

'She gave you no reason for refusal? She asked your advice, did she not? But I must not ask these questions. I see that. I see that.'

'Can I get you more coffee?'

Wainwright looked with dismayed amazement at the drained cup he dandled in front of him, then held it out. Harrington took his time with pot, milk jug, sugar tongs. He placed the replenished cup at the professor's side, and turning his back saw to his own drink.

'I think she loves you, Joe,' Wainwright croaked.

'I hadn't noticed it.' Why did he lie?

'I think it's the truth.'

'Is that why you advised her to move in with me?'

'I didn't know, then. Only that she admired you. I thought your example might stir her.' His fingers grasped the air in front of him. 'It's only since she rebuffed me that I, that I. . . .'

Harrington waited. For nothing. He shook his head.

'No, Paul. Nowhere near the truth.'

'Are you sure?'

'As I can be. We get on well.'

'Joe, have you had sex with Helen Southwell?' His mouth gaped at the effrontery of his own question. 'No, no. I mustn't ask you that.'

'The answer is "No".'

'You'd say that in any case, wouldn't you?'

The conversation suddenly sobered Wainwright who sat straighter, crossed his legs, addressing himself only to his replenished cup of coffee. Helen had told him, he whispered, that Harrington's house had belonged to the family. Joe explained the circumstances.

'What did you father do?'

'He was an electrical engineer by profession, but he moved into admin. He came up here on loan during the war to expand some departments attached to the R.O.F. . . .'

'R.O.F.? What's that?' Wainwright, earnest to dispel ignorance.

'Royal Ordnance Factory.'

'Oh, I see.'

'And then after the war, his own firm, Twentyman Drew, built new factories here, and in Derby and Loughborough, and he was in charge of the district, and further north and west, until the late sixties, when he went back to headquarters. I was fourteen. My sister had just married, and took over the house. I bought it from her.'

'Was your father at all like you, Joe?'

'Not to my recollection. Why do you ask?'

'He seems to have got things done. At least he passed that on to his son.'

'He worked hard enough. My mother always said he knew exactly what he could get the workforce to do, and what he couldn't.'

'Is he still alive?'

'No. Neither of my parents.'

'Would you say he had any influence on you?' Wainwright asked questions with ease.

'Couldn't fail, could he? He'd talk to me, and take me out now and again when he was at home. He looked at my reports. He gave me advice. Sensible, if I remember. A clever, dry chap, in his forties when I was born. He didn't fling his weight about, but if you argued with him you had to be sure of your facts. But he was busy, and the business of bringing me up fell on my mother, and my sister who was nearly ten years older than I was. Two mothers, really.'

'They didn't come from this part of the world?'

'No, Londoners. Though my sister and I were both born in this house.'

'I like the look of the place, Joe. You're fortunate. You are indeed. Beautiful, and out of the way. Don't you think of rearing a family some time? This would be the ideal. Plenty of room, big grounds, yet not too far from the town. Aren't you the marrying sort, then?'

'I've been married once.'

'Oh, yes. I think I knew that. I must have done.'

'To Paulina Street.'

It was immediately obvious that the name meant nothing to Wainwright. He looked up, a keen student, ready to be enlightened.

'She's a television star.'

'Oh.'

The face did not brighten; Wainwright found no interest there.

'I've been thinking about children since I proposed to Helen. I'm too old to be a father, don't you think? Not physically, if you know what I mean. But at sixty-three. Perhaps that's why Helen Southwell wouldn't consider me. One reason, anyhow. You didn't have any children by your marriage to this television lady, did you? I suppose one is missing something.'

'We're all missing something. If one's a man one's missing being a woman. Or I'm missing being an airline pilot or a cabinet minister or a murderer. There are thousands of things we cannot be.'

'Would you not like to pass your name on or your genetic endowment?

'No.'

'That does surprise me, Joe. Did your father ever try to influence you towards the sciences? My father was a wholesale grocer, and what he would dearly have loved to be was a Wesleyan Methodist minister. Given today's opportunities he would have been a doctor of divinity. He took a great pride in the fact that I had become a professor. He never abbreviated the title, on a letter, for instance.'

'You brought him pleasure, then,' Harrington said, dismissing them all.

Wainwright was launched, accepted more coffee and a large slice of fruitcake. He slouched in his chair, conveying his enjoyment, speaking easily of his childhood, his father's books, his first bicycle, Sunday school treats. For twenty minutes he spoke of his home, his mother, his schools. 'I was smothered with ambitious love.' He was never bullied at school, never left home without his parents until he tried for, and won, an Oxford scholarship. University and the army had made a different man of him, but only on the surface. 'There was nothing I wanted that I could not have.' His demands, of course, were always reasonable, but his parents sacrificed and encouraged, and he rewarded them with his prizes, degrees, his position. He spoke with warmth, affording himself a wealth of pleasure by his recital. Harrington, surprised, not displeased by this display, asked about religious faith.

'I had lost it at school. I made no fuss and continued to attend service, but my parents raised no objection when sometimes I said I wanted to stay at home to study. That seemed sensible. They were not bigoted people, but to them, brought up in the faith, chapel represented beauty and intellect. An exposition of a Greek New Testament verse, a developed conceit or metaphor in a sermon gave my father enormous satisfaction, and some of the ministers when I was a boy were scholarly in every sense. A sermon represented hours of study, of reading, of comparison, of experience applied to learning. I know you think it was all tub-thumping, Bible-punching, ranting evangelism. We had our share of that, I admit, but perhaps we were exceptionally lucky, or perhaps because men of my father's mind had a hand in choice of ministers, we had two or three men in my boyhood who were educators, intellectuals in the best sense.'

'But they lost you?'

'Yes. I lost the ground of my belief. I could see no necessity for God, a god, and I was replacing one sort of literature, biblical, with another, secular equivalent from my classics and English.'

'You did that without trouble?' Harrington pressed.

'Yes. I was arrogant, but not outwardly. I found I neither believed in a divine creator nor a benign providence, but I said nothing. No great religious demands were made on me, at least by my parents. Perhaps they realized for all my tact what I felt.'

'You grew away from them?'

'My father and mother? In some senses, yes. In many, I suppose. But I don't think, as a personality, I differ much from my father. I deal with literary texts and examinations as he dealt with sugar or potatoes. But above these commodities he pursued his inspirations, his study and exegesis. In the same way I am never satisfied with my working life in its humdrum sense. I reach beyond it, as he did.'

It did not take Wainwright long to reach the pains and *longueurs* of a professor's life, the committees, the struggles for place and power, the cabals, quarrels, incessant barter that occupied the hours he should have spent on scholarship. Harrington had heard this times enough before, but this evening's practice had softened the old man's verbal stiffness, anointed him into a genial malice, so that though nobody, neither registrar nor professor of engineering (particular cronies) escaped censure, it amused the listener. Illustrative anecdotes were well chosen; the vice chancellor, a humourless bureaucrat, having tripped, fortunately on to his feet, down six marble stairs, had bowed to two typists watching the sudden, ignominious descent and murmured as he glided unperturbed away, 'How are the mighty fallen.' The dean of sciences had removed at his own expense a wall to double the size of his office, already larger than the v.c.'s, and had then meekly followed his wife as she had chosen, and supervised the laying of, a wall-to-wall carpet. 'He got away with it because he convinced the bursar and the estates people that he needed a room large enough to entertain local businessmen, and as he was paying for it himself, and the alterations were

102

structurally sound, this piece of egomania was allowed.' Wainwright attempted an imitation of his colleague: 'You and I don't notice such matters, but these people do. Status, accoutrements count; equipment. One phone is no good; one computer screen is nothing, worse than nothing. And I need something out of these people. Unto him, they say, that hath shall be given. My department is not, and never will be entirely inside the university.'

The professor enjoyed himself, Harrington with him. Wainwright ate two slices of apple pie with cream. He spoke about his mother's puddings, her baking of bread, and dropped a sentence: 'If I could write one good poem it would concern my childhood and the happiness I felt.' When Joe asked if this was the reason he had concentrated on medieval literature, Wainwright narrowed his eyes, answered without emphasis, 'My scholarly pursuits have never touched the real man.'

At ten minutes to midnight Wainwright left, had his usual difficulty starting the car, then edged off down the road. His final words from the front seat, 'Think about what I said. About Helen Southwell', were accompanied by prods at the accelerator.

Harrington, chores completed, made his way upstairs pleased with life, as if he'd ferreted out some source of human warmth. He tried to whistle the duet from *Zauberflöte*.

11

Spring was in no hurry.

At the end of February, on an evening of frost after sunshine, Harrington found a foolscap envelope through his door. 'By hand. J. J. Harrington, Esq., M.A., Ph.D.' proclaimed block capitals. Inside were twelve typewritten sheets, with title page. 'An Incident'. There was neither author's name nor accompanying note, but he recognized Thomas Reeves's typewriter. He read the first paragraph. A young man of seventeen walked along an avenue, touching each lime tree, peering at the odd numbers on garden gates, checking the time with his wristwatch. The flickering of a street lamp threw shadows; a sickle moon seemed bright but ineffective. The young man, excited, listened to the jingle in his head: In March, July, October, May/ The nones are seventh, the ides the fifteenth day. He leaned against the wall of number twenty-seven trying to read the name on the sign which swung on chain from the roof of the porch. He crept up the short drive. Alma Villa. He tiptoed back careful not to let the latch click.

Harrington smiled to himself and, interested, did not read further. He replaced the sheets in the envelope. That day he had found time to speak to Helen about Wainwright's visit. She had seemed displeased, on the defensive, as if he poked fun at her.

'What do you make of that?' he had asked her.

'I don't like it,' she said, teeth clenched, turning her back.

'He made a most favourable impression on me, for once.'

'You've no idea how you can hurt people,' she answered. 'No idea at all.' Her voice lacked power. 'Just because Paul acts or talks foolishly it doesn't mean that he has no feelings.

And what sort of man are you to sit in judgement when you come straight out and say that I love you?'

'That's what he claimed.'

'You could have kept quiet about it,' she answered.

'It's an important part of what he thinks, his reason why you refused him.'

'But what do I feel, then?' Her voice had an edge of shrillness. 'You don't consider that.'

'It's not true, Helen. You don't love me. I wanted to be honest with you, because I liked Wainwright for once. He seemed to be trying to say what he felt. He was not handing out one of your little prepackaged pieces of thought. It impressed me. I concluded. . . .'

'Concluded. Don't you realise how banal your words are? Sludge?'

'I wanted you to know, Helen, what had happened. I'm sorry if it's upset you.'

'Upset. Upset. I sometimes think, Joe, that you're hardly a human being.'

'That's not very fair.'

'You don't know much about fairness for that matter.'

'I'm sorry, Helen. I thought you'd like to hear what he said. I had no idea it would affect you in this way.'

'That's what I'm telling you.'

She waited for his reply, which did not come. Harrington would not justify himself. Helen stood, in her accusatory silence. In the end she slipped out closing the door without noise. As he stared down at the papers on his desk, he was unsure whether she had gone or not.

At lunch he had run into Wainwright, had stopped, announced that he had enjoyed their conversation and invited the professor to visit him again. Wainwright shuffled, narrowed his eyes shiftily, staggered across the corridor as he mouthed his thanks and made rapidly off, hand to a harassed face. Harrington could not manage the right thing today. Back at his books, he found Blake opened at the conversation with the prophets Isaiah and Ezekiel.

'Then I asked: "Does a firm persuasion that a thing is so, make it so?"

He replied: "All poets believe that it does, and in ages of imagination this firm persuasion removed mountains; but many are not capable of a firm persuasion of anything." '

Harrington marked himself down as one incapable. A student fortunately interrupted him, to hand in an essay on Johnson's criticisms of Gray. The five minutes of conversation – and he delayed the girl for the space of a few sentences – relieved him so that he could begin to work again.

Helen did not reappear, neither in the room, nor at the lunch table. He felt vaguely guilty. As he was preparing his evening meal, two large salad sandwiches, Anne Selby telephoned, apologizing for her father's outburst over the telephone, about which she had only just heard.

'Did he still sound cross?'

'Yes, but that's typical. Whenever he goes over anything in his mind, his blood boils again.'

'I think he's forgiven me.'

'Why do you say that?'

'He's just sent me another typescript for consideration.'

'When?'

'Today. By hand.'

She smacked her lips in exasperation, and then announced ingenuously that she was blushing.

'Is it any good?' she muttered.

'I haven't read it yet.'

'He's a devious devil,' Anne answered. 'I only heard about all this last night, and he never said a word about sending you another piece. He's a sly-boots.'

'I don't know what time the thing arrived because I've been out all day. But it's quite possible, isn't it?, that his conversation with you goaded him into typing this out, if not actually writing it, and then dashing round with it.'

'I shall never understand him. He's not straight. Not with me, or anybody else.' A snort of embarrassment escaped her. 'That's a dreadful thing to say about my own father, isn't it? But it's true. He takes you into his confidence when he wants

106

something from you.' She waited for his comments which were not forthcoming. 'You wouldn't talk about your father like that, would you?'

'He's dead.'

'I feel so guilty about him. He does such unpleasant, unnecessary things. He writes screeds to my mother, all sorts of accusations about events that happened, were over years ago. She dreads them. Teddy, her present husband, tells her to throw them straight into the fire, without opening them, but she can't. They were married twenty years, after all. It must mean something. What, I don't know.'

Anne laughed again, but quietly, keeping it from her family.

'How's Tony?' Harrington inquired.

'He's more mobile, and that means he's better tempered. I shall be glad, I can tell you, when he's back to normal.'

'You'll need a holiday.'

'Yes, but I shan't get one. I never go out on my own. I did join a W.E.A. class on psychology, but I've had to pack it in.'

'That's a pity.'

'You can say that again.'

Anne Selby offered a further brief sentence of apology for her father and put the phone down as if she'd been interrupted. He ought to have invited her round, but he wanted to work that evening.

He had taken one bite of his sandwich when the telephone erupted. Helen.

'I've been trying to ring you before, but the line was engaged.'

'Yes.'

'It's about what we were saying this morning.'

'Yes.'

Silence on a telephone stoked up awkwardness.

'In view of what's happened I think I should move out.'

'There's no need for that, Helen.'

'On your part, no. I want to get away.'

Harrington considered. He stared in distaste at the bitten

107

sandwich on the telephone table. He had not realized he had carried it out.

'I beg you not to do . . . anything like that . . . well, just yet.'

'What did you say?'

He repeated his sentence, exactly, more fluently, wondering what mental turmoil hindered her hearing.

'Why?' Snapped at him, like a ruptured fiddle string.

'I seem to have hurt you, Helen. I did not mean to. Even now I'm running over our conversation to try to remember where and how I could have been so, so,' he floundered, 'uncaring.' That sounded hollow, artificial.

'If you can't see, it's no use my. . . .'

'No, Helen. You're the best, most co-operative, considerate roommate I've known. I don't want to lose you.'

'It's not what you want, now. It's what I want.'

'Would you please put off the decision for a day or two?'

'Why should I? Let me get out and forget about it, get it behind me.'

'Just give it a few days. Helen, you've shaken me. I can't realize what it is I've done.'

'Won't, you mean.'

'Perhaps, but I ask you. Give me a week, then, Helen. I can't tell you how bitterly sorry I am.'

'You don't even know where you've gone wrong.'

'A week's grace, Helen. To see if we can come to some accommodation. All those books to be humped somewhere else, all the. . . .'

'Shifting a few hundred books is the least of it.'

He despaired.

'A week, Helen. To find out if you can. . . .'

She had put down the telephone, gently, decisively. He listened, angrily alert, to make sure, then flicked through his file for her number. That, in his careful hand, seemed written in some foreign, accusatory dialect. Six figures represented her smart, his puzzlement. Replacing the telephone, he picked up his sandwich. His arms hung streaked with pain; he snatched at a fallen crumb. In his mouth it had size and texture, but was without taste. He stood in the hall, legs pressed against the table, willing that submissive woman, or anybody else, to call him, to recall him to the circle of humanity. None obliged. He did not budge. There was no relief in a chilly hall on a February evening.

Harrington ate, cleared, worked for three hours pen in hand rereading *The Castle of Otranto*. He ended with a series of quotations and a hint of a generalization, none the wiser. Trying to find a modern equivalent, in status and quality or lack of it, he quickly named a dozen; he found no comfort in the consideration of tomorrow evening's task, *Vathek*. What annoyed him was the certainty that he knew already what he thought about these books before he opened them. Minor literature is likely to remain unimportantly and properly dock-eted. Why should he expect these novels to reveal some new vista of understanding? He had not lost his intellectual balance to that extent, though he regretted such temperate views. At thirty-two he was already a Laodicean; he had another thirty-two years to become a Wainwright. As he splashed boiling water on to his instant coffee, he knew he had advanced far on the way. He did not relish the idea; he would not, he resolved, give up reading.

He pulled Thomas Reeves's typescript from its envelope, searching once more for a covering note. There was none. Again the seventeen-year-old dawdled, ahead of himself, along the dark street. He had no name; the pronoun sufficed. He knocked, hurting his knuckles, on the front door of number fifty-five as soon as his cheap wristwatch signalled the hour. The small porch was walled half way up with dark tiles. A woman let him in. The narrow hallway smelt of cooking without being warm. Two miles away, from the south, the Council House clock chimed.

'You've come, then,' the woman said. She was called Betty; the boy thought of her as Bet. 'What did you tell your mam?'

'That I was going out.'

'Where, though?'

'To see a friend.'

'You could put it like that.'

109

Reeves described the woman in some detail, her dark hair, bundled, not kempt but held by a red comb. Her eyes were dark, liquid; the skin beneath them brusied. Her dress, sulphur-yellow with a wide white collar, hung loose on the breadth of her shoulder. Her fingers were red, almost chapped. She wore no stockings, but her feet were deep inside pink, ankle-high slippers, grubbily the worse for wear.

Harrington stopped reading, after a time, to ask himself what Reeves wanted from this description. There was a coarseness about her, her pendulous breasts, wide hips; she had clearly made no attempt to dress up for the visitor, but she had powdered her flat, sallow face and wore perfume. Reeves gave her age as thirty-eight, but said she looked older. To the boy? The author? She had dark hairs on her forearms; a wedding ring and two blue-glass earrings were her only jewellery. A clock in the body of a china dog ticked on the mantelpiece. Bet, enigmatically smiling, rose and poked, then mended the fire, and while on her feet asked if the young man wanted a cup of tea. She seemed affronted at his refusal, and walked about the room, touching and straightening chairs or objects on the sideboard.

Reeves for the second time described the place in detail. Again Harrington was reminded of the literary care of the essayists of the twenties, men with Latin and Greek, a respect for their craft and a realization that their readers shared the enjoyment of sharp observation distilled into measured sentences, complex but graspable paragraphs, here and there to be surprised or enlivened with the flash of paradox. Reeves's school had drilled him into good order. The firelight, in spite of the bare electric bulb under its pot Chinese-coolie shade, danced on the far wall; the wall clock, nearly twenty minutes fast, struck the half-hour with a metallic flatness, as if someone had dropped a small saucepan on a quarry-tiled floor.

Harrington decided that Reeves's taste had been formed in a time when one read more slowly, had the leisure to savour. And yet the exercise seemed trivial, what Eliot had called 'a solemn game'. It was not exactly boring, or no more so than the Miltonics of James Thomson, or even Shakespeare's euphuistic brilliance, but he could not take it seriously. Yet the style presented to Reeves the manner in which a confession, hidden away for fifty years, was to be delivered. Old-fashioned, cumbersome, written with a steel nib dipped in an inkwell, it affected to be literature, the best words in the best order.

'Come over here,' Bet had ordered. Standing with her back to the fire she did not use the youth's Christian name. His shoulders rippling with shivers, like a mountain stream, 'swift in its shallows', the young man rose, approached her. 'Kiss me,' she commanded; her explicit order, Reeves would have called it 'injunction', clashed crudely with the syntax around it. The boy complied, a yard in front of the leaping fire, in the heat of the room. Reeves, obedient to the rules of literary composition, abandoned the young lover with Bet's tongue deep in his mouth, while he described the woman's background, her husband, the miner and political speaker, her lack of children, her humdrum job in a hairdressing salon.

They had met three days before on a Sunday afternoon in Southwell Minster, where the boy had explained the features of Norman architecture to her. She had dropped her handbag in the nave and the youth had ducked to help pick up the scattered contents. He had blushed, then diffidently began to shuffle away until she bombarded him with questions, confessing her ignorance. Within ten minutes he had walked at his ease, offering explanations, laying down the law.

Reeves described the Norman splendour, 'sincerity in stone', he had called it, the delicacy of the chancel, the bravura of the chapterhouse carving. She had questioned him thoroughly, though she held and consulted a small guide book against which she tested his knowledge. The two had walked out of the minster talking still, recovered their cycles, set out and after a mile or so had parked under an oak tree where she had produced not very appetising fish-paste sandwiches and a flask of tea. The boy ate without relish though he was hungry, having 'devoured' his own sandwiches soon after midday. Reeves described the fields, clouds, the sunshine,

111

shadows on bright grass, the sounds of summer in the hedge-bottom. The writer had looked carefully, and so much so that Harrington wondered whether this was real memory or whether the man had recently been back to fill his notebook with relevant detail. That would have been last summer at the latest. Had Reeves been preparing this for some months? Harrington decided that this piece of work had been completed in the last few weeks, in reply to his critical appraisal of the extract from the memoir.

Bucolic air hung warm and heavy though there were no indications of storm; sounds of humanity were few and distant. Fluffs of cloud sailed across the azure of the sky, but beneath the trees no wind disturbed.

The woman questioned the boy again, this time about his studies. He described the poems in *The Oxford Book of French Verse*, the two books of Virgil, *Hamlet*, selected essays of William Hazlitt, especially 'On First Acquaintance with Poets' and 'On the Pleasures of Painting' which he studied for Higher Certificate. She had seemed avid for his knowledge, pressing him to continue, calling out her wonderment. They had books in their house, her husband was a great reader, but none of these, only political things and economics pamphlets. The young man spoke fluently: invited to instruct at length for the first time in his life, he made the effort to impress. He had not been able to speak about his studies in this way to his parents who, if interested, showed caution, demonstrating at once that such high learning was beyond them.

At the same time the woman sat carelessly. As she reached for flask or grease proof paper, she would leave her legs wide, baring stocking tops, suspenders, thighs, pale lemon knickers. The boy could not be sure whether she tempted him or whether her interest in his account of his education grew so great that it did not cross her mind that she acted unchastely. Perhaps, the excited youngster snatched at the thought, she had concluded that one so learned would not be touched by lust. Once she caught him staring up her legs and drew her

112

frock over her knees but without hurry, embarrassment or comment.

She had been the first to move, scrambling up, straightening her dress, saying she had promised to go out that evening with her husband. Grinning, she had held a hand out to him, hauled him to his feet, then kissed him. Her scent overpowered him; her mouth tasted of the fish paste; he hugged her, fondled her buttocks, but she broke away, amused still.

'Naughty, naughty.' She pointed comically to her haunches. 'That belongs to me. Come here.' She produced a handkerchief, which she wrapped on a forefinger to wet with her tongue, as she advanced. 'Let's remove the evidence.' She scrubbed his lips and face, like a mother, showing her handkerchief pink with lipstick. 'You're a little devil.' Vulgarly.

In no time they were out of the field 'bowling along' the deserted roads. Not until they reached the suburbs did she invite him to her house. 'Come on Wednesday at seven.' She gave him the address, asked if he'd remember it. He said he was not sure; on Wednesday evenings he was busy; that was Roman history and English essay night. 'Please yourself,' she had said. Her legs pedalling, had shone strongly calved, muscular. Soon afterwards she turned almost hurriedly off, and he was left freewheeling down an urban road, out of his way, with a Latin prose to complete.

Harrington, slightly put out with the constant literary delays and the deliberate archness of language, flicked through the concluding pages. The woman unbuttoned her dress to the belt, pushed the strap of her slip down her arm, lifted out her right breast, then reaching covered the large nipple with her lover's hand. Reeves felt fire on his trouser legs; her eyes were shut. He had not examined or handled a woman's breast before; he could barely breathe. She had no sooner opened his fly buttons, stroked his penis briefly than he ejaculated.

The woman squawked, swore at him, then laughed, as if 'released from some enchantment'.

'Have you got a handkerchief?' she demanded. She dabbed at his flesh, trousers, her soiled dress, the pegged rug. 'Put it away,' she ordered, pointing. Her breast had disappeared back inside the straightened, not yet fastened clothes. 'You're a big boy now.'

The typescript spent a half-page on the time they sat together on either side of the fire, talking again about books. The woman seemed to have dismissed what had happened and questioned him about the construction of the 'massy pillars' in the nave of the minster and then about the pleasures of being able to speak French. He had never visited the country, saw no liklihood of so doing, but her obvious envy of his mastery of these foreign sounds reassured him. He trembled still; the skin of his back shuddered like released elastic. She did not notice his discomposure; without tenderness, her local accent strong, she continued her catechism. 'What's French for "cup of tea"? "Milk Jug"?. "Husband"? Has that got anything to do with marrying.'

She looked surprised when he said he had to leave, but made no attempt to detain him, merely inspecting him as he stood, remarking, 'You've got some stuff on your trousers.' Fetching in a leisurely way a wet cloth from the kitchen, she cleaned him up quickly, asexually, with, 'It'll soon dry.' She patted his shoulder, did not kiss him, as he left the house.

Again the boy walked the lamp-lit street. Excitement and revulsion fought in him. He counted himself as quite different from the one who less than an hour before had peered at the numbers. Pride and self-hatred stopped him so that he clung to the stone wall of a front garden. A groan split out of him, against his will, his nature. A bare breast, spilt semen, reduced not only his morality but his power of ratiocination. For the second time he stared along the path at the porch of number twenty-seven, humiliated as if he had been physically beaten, but without the pain.

Harrington refolded the typescript.

Was this an account of a real incident, or a piece of wild pornography written to attract or mock the reader? He could not decide; after this first perusal the talk about books rather

114

than the sexual exchange had brought the best out of the author, but that doubtless could be attributed to the method. The final paragraph, when shame predominated over excitement, had power, with the dark-treed spaces between gas lamps, the unlighted front doors, the closed gates and shadowed gardens personifying the secrets the young man had so nearly discovered.

Harrington wrote the date on the envelope, slipped it into a drawer in his desk upstairs. He wondered what Anne would think of her father's adventure. The woman, if she was still alive, would be eighty-nine now. Had Reeves in his sick exertions on the Burma–Siam railway thought of Bet, taken any comfort from her? Had he run across her after the war and had they found anything to say to each other? Had the seventeen-year-old ventured round to the dark house in the dark street again?

The narrative did not lack appeal, but its literary faults, unacceptable choices rather than lapses, its many loose ends attracted more strongly than its successes. Harrington, only too aware of the academic's giving with the left as he took away with the right, smirked his own cleverness or decency out of the way and put his mind elsewhere. He would talk to Reeves later about a writer's responsibility to a reader.

Edgy still, he pulled on his top coat and scarf, walked the length of the garden and let himself out of the back gate. The street beyond still retained the appearance of the country road it had been eighty years ago when his house was built. Big trees, limes and sycamores, suggested perhaps a carriage drive to Stanton Hall; two elms had been recently felled. The dull weather seemed unpleasantly cold still; he had forgotten his gloves. He quickened his pace, made for the private estate of new building half a mile back. There concrete standards flooded the neatness of streets with an orange light and the downstairs windows of a majority of houses glowed though it was now half past eleven. The deserted streets looked prosperous; second cars stood in the drives. Double garages were almost as common as flowering cherry trees; rose bushes, pruned or untouched, abounded.

115

A car drew up fifty yards away. All four doors opened. A radio gashed the silence. Four men appeared, crowding the exterior of the car, pitching their row against the blare of the car radio, before staggering along the path to the house. One pair held each other up, exaggerating the difficulty of walking by an acutely angled zigzag motion. From the street door a female voice begged the revellers to shush, to think of the neighbours, and the men responded by passing the message loudly round while one bawled out that it was 'Love, love, love.' Back on the road a woman walked round the vehicle, making certain the doors were locked, and then waited, oddly with an elbow on the car roof, for Harrington to come up. The men by this time had bundled themselves indoors, with little diminution of racket.

'A celebration,' the woman said to Harrington.

'So I see.' He had stopped. 'Birthday?'

'Wedding,' she answered. 'It's a stag party. I've just had to drive them up from the pub. And a fine state they'll be in for the ceremony, I don't think. Ridiculous, in't it?'

'Well.'

'Well. What's a well without a bucket?' Her childish riposte seemed to satisfy, silence her, though she maintained her relaxed position, a young woman in her early thirties, trim, not pretty.

'It doesn't happen often,' he said.

'Second time in his case. My brother. My husband's one of the others.' She moved her left hand almost formally to within eighteen inches of her face and looked down on her broad wedding ring. 'You married?'

'Not now.'

'You lived to regret it, did you? I do sometimes.'

Harrington did not answer that. He could not understand why she had stayed out in the street for this exchange.

'Lovely girl she is. And he'll have a hangover in the morning that'll split his head into two big parts. She'll make him draw his horns in, though. At least I hope she will. Plenty about her. He's not a bad lad, but he never settled to his first marriage. Did you have any children?'

116

'No.'

'That's a blessing. I've got three.' She pointed towards a bedroom window. 'All asleep up there, unless them daft sods haven't woken 'em up. And they'll be playing it up at seven tomorrow morning, come what may. I sometimes ask myself what I am doing with my life.' She drummed with a small, tightly closed fist on the car roof. 'Better get inside to see what they've broken.'

She wished him good night, still in the same unemphatic voice, marched along the path, let herself in.

Bedroom lights came on. He walked a silent street out in the cold.

12

Harrington was surprised to receive a note from Paulina's husband.

'From Lord Benson' read the printed legend at the top of the stationery.

Dear Joe,

I write because Paulina seems to be worrying herself about you. I do not think this is a misjudgement on my part, as almost every day and often more than once, she makes some remarks about your health or your state of mind. I have tried to get out of her what it is which so concerns her. Her answer is always much the same: 'I suppose I feel guilty.' Again I may be wrong but I think she is genuinely exercised about you. I would, therefore, be grateful if you could send her a line to reassure her that there is nothing seriously wrong. I find it quite unnerving to have to ask this of you, but I think you will understand.

With best wishes.

Yours sincerely,

Edmond.

Harrington read the missive twice, kept it in his inside pocket, and glanced over it during the day. He made as little plain sense of it as he did of Reeves's 'Incident'. It was possible that Benson and Paulina were beginning to quarrel and the husband took this unusual course as a reaction of some sort, but a letter dispatched to his wife's former husband hardly seemed a cure for an unsatisfactory marriage. Perhaps Benson was committing adultery, or Paulina for that matter. He could not come up with an explanation, and decided to postpone his reply.

Helen Southwell did not appear in their room, though she was, he knew, about the university. Presumably she had collected the books she needed while he was out at a lecture. Her action stung him; childishly he rearranged the three piles of books on her desk.

After lunch Paul Wainwright waited for him.

'Ah, Joe.' With a finger lifted he gave the appearance of a man afflicted with a brilliant but unwelcome idea. 'Next week, next week. Were you thinking of attending Thomas Trevor's lecture? The poet?'

'I was.' Why had the old idiot needed to explain that Trevor was a poet? Perhaps he feared he'd misremembered the name.

'Would you consider taking the chair?'

'Aren't you going to be there, then?'

'Oh, yes. I would not think of missing the occasion. But you are our modern man. Your introduction would carry more weight than anything I might say.'

'I see.'

'You lecture on Yeats and Eliot and Wallace Stevens.'

'Harold lectures on Hardy and Lowell and Lawrence.'

'Will you do it?' Wainwright banged his question down.

'If that's what you want.' He sounded ashamed.

'Good. Good man. Trevor's an old fellow of your college, isn't he? I thought it would be most suitable. Now listen. We'll need to wine and dine Trevor, and I suggest you and I and Dr Southwell form a small party. I'll consult you or her about the food and the drink. I'm trying to get the v.c. to the lecture. With his wife. Lady Cross is interested in literature, as you know.'

The professor pulled in his lips.

'Put the date into your diary.'

'I've already done so,'

'Of course, of course. But the time will be different now, earlier.'

He edged away, with no words of thanks, considering he had done Harrington a favour. He turned back ten yards on.

'Do you own any of Trevor's publications? Perhaps you could make a loan of one to me.'

'I'll need to look at it myself.'

'Ah, yes.'

'The library has the collected. . . .'

'Library.' Wainwright was already on his way, mouthing the password.

Harrington found it difficult to reply civilly to Wainwright, even when the man talked sense. It was possible that this invitation represented his approval, gave the younger man a chance to shine in front of the vice chancellor, hinted at promotion, though that was unlikely in these days of retrenchment.

On the following day he met Helen scurrying along the path to the library building. She hesitated for a step or two.

'Are we speaking?' he asked.

'Yes.'

'Has Paul said anything about this Trevor lecture?'

'He sent me a note.'

'Are you able to go?'

'Yes.'

She looked young, like a student, a pile of books clutched to her green tweed coat.

'I wondered if you were doing anything this weekend? If you'd come round Saturday for lunch? Or dinner, if it suits you better?'

Helen shifted from foot to foot, almost formally.

'I don't know what to say, Joe.'

'Try "yes". It's nearly as easy as "no".'

She frowned at his facetiousness, stared him straight in the eye.

'I'm just managing to come to terms with things as far as you and I are concerned,' she announced. 'I don't want to rock the boat.'

'I'll be diplomacy itself.' She did not raise a smile. 'If you come for lunch early we could go out for an hour or two before it's too dark.'

'You'll be wasting a good working day.'

'Leave me to be the judge of that.'

She jerked her head at his change of tone.

'What time, then?'

'Half-twelve.'

120

'Yes. Thank you. Yes.'

She hitched up her burden of books, clacked past him on high heels.

Harrington finished the day in his office with a note to Lord Benson, thanking him for his letter, saying he did not see his way clear to write to Paulina, who now owed him nothing. He was, however, both fit and open to argument. Sincerely. The short side of paper seemed typical of his present malaise, neither here nor there, unpleasant for the sake of it. He typed the address and rang Tom Reeves.

'What did you think of it, then?' Reeves bit off his question with a laugh.

'Interesting in parts.'

'Which parts?' Again the lewd snigger. 'Bit more in your line, eh?'

Harrington, very carefully, without hurry, flat-voiced, expounded his criticisms. He tried not to condesdend, to treat the typescript as a student's examination piece. Reeves heard him out, and paused before he answered with a question of his own.

'Do you mean to say you are more interested in what I said about school and lessons than about the sex?'

'Yes, put roughly.'

'Is that your fault or mine? I mean, aren't you interested in women? This actually happened to me. Out of the blue. In days when there wasn't an excess of promiscuity. To a schoolboy who imagined it might happen, but never expected it in a thousand years.'

'I understand that.'

'Understand? Understand? I doubt if you do. I doubt it very much.'

'I'm not speaking of the experience, Mr Reeves. I'm talking about the text I had in front of me.'

Again, he progressed through his rigmarole, without speed, apologizing that 'An Incident' was not on the desk before him.

'We'll have to take some of it sentence by sentence. Or that's the way, ideally.'

121

'Is it worth it?' Reeves dyspeptically.

'That depends on you, Mr Reeves.'

'Whether I learn from what you're telling me, you mean.'

'Whether you're prepared to keep an open mind. I go through texts with my students in this way. Some profit from it, some don't.'

'They haven't written what you're studying. That makes a difference.' A catch of breath, as if he'd been elightened. 'Or does it?'

By the time the conversation dragged itself to a conclusion, Reeves spoke with a kind of weary pessimism, convinced that nothing he could write would please Harrington. They did not arrange a meeting face to face. Harrington felt wintry resignation, but occupied himself usefully until home time.

Edmond Benson replied by return, apologetically, saying he had not been quite straight, that he had felt uncertain about Paulina who 'was uncooperative sometimes and withdrawn', and he had, therefore, chanced the approach to Harrington. What he had said, about her talk of guilt, for example, was the truth as far as it went, but was really an excuse. He hoped he would be forgiven writing like this; things were not near desperation by any means, and, to be honest, he did not quite know why he had written as he had. It must have been on impulse. He hoped he would be pardoned. Sincerely.

This was followed a day later by a note from Paulina. She had recognized the handwriting on his reply to Edmond, and at her inquiries her husband had confessed, and had allowed her to read copies (she followed this with three exclamation marks) of his letters and Harrington's reply. Edmond, she considered, was in many ways naïve (he would not be allowed to read that) and made a mountain out of a molehill.

The next paragraph admitted that the marriage was strained, but that she put down to her own dissatisfaction in the theatre. Her stage and television work kept her intensely occupied, out every night, away from home two, sometimes three, days a week, and compensated only financially. 'I cannot make Edmond see this,' she complained. 'He bluntly avers that I am coining a great deal of money in a profession where unemployment is the norm, and cannot see that artistic satisfaction has any part. Sometimes he even tries to make a principle out of this, telling me that Shakespeare took up popular genres and made artistic successes of these. We have rows about this. They're not much like the quarrels we used to have, Joe, because he argues as if he's in a law court and even talks in a sniffy way that's nothing like his normal voice. It makes me furious, and I slam doors, and stamp my feet, and then he apologizes, oh so politely, and that makes me worse. He always ends in the same reasonable [more exclamation marks] tone that whenever I am tired of the theatre, I can retire and help him spend his money. I shout at him and ask him where my independence would be then, but he looks hurt and worries and corrugates his brow and says that's the last thing he'd take from me, even if he could.'

The final side of the letter admitted that something had gone, was going awry, that she, rereading, sounded as bad as Edmond. She guessed that both of them had made a 'song and dance' where none was necessary, but she worried that Edmond had 'acted so out of character' in writing to Joe. 'Either I don't understand him or. . . .' She had broken off there with a dramatic series of inky dabs and then continued, 'I don't understand him. Stop.' At that she sent her love but added a postscript that she did not want advice but was only working off her 'ill temper and unease. Forgive me. P.S.' Even in her distress she used the small, joky literary device.

Harrington read the letter twice, and again during the evening, and decided he would not reply. Anne Selby telephoned to say that she had spoken to her father who had appeared excited, stimulated by Harrington's latest criticism.

'Is it worth reading?' she asked.

'Yes. Though not quite for the reasons he intended.'

'That sounds bad. You mean he doesn't know what he's doing.'

'In a sense, though I guess this is so with all writing.'

'You don't mean that, do you?'

He was in no mood for explanations and brushed her off,

asking about her husband's health. Things became gradually easier at home, she answered: Tony could hobble about and drive himself so that she felt comparatively cheerful.

At the university he kept his exchanges with Helen Southwell short, pleasant, businesslike. Wainwright was holding a last departmental conference about papers for the final examinations, and appeared here at his best. For once, he laid down the law to some effect. Secretive, he had evolved a system.

Fairly early in the first term the professor announced who was to be responsible for this paper or that; Harrington's allocation this year was 1700–1830 and 1880 to the present day. Those 'with an interest', i.e. teaching, had to submit questions to the 'setters of papers' before Christmas, and copies of completed papers with rubrics were handed in on the first day of the second term to the professor. Setters were allowed to keep one copy only and this not at the university. Breakage of this rule called down thunder. Wainwright, red and mottled of face, would bawl out, quite out of character and even publicly, transgressors, however senior they were. 'Even a bloody fool can see the reasons for these rules,' he shouted. 'I am not going to have students discussing finals questions from January onwards in this department.' Those who failed to comply could be certain that unwanted end-of-term chores would be directed their way; about examinations Wainwright, an easy-going man, became both aggressive and unpleasant. No one knew the reasons for this; some suggested that he had been affected by some scandal early in his career.

Then, meetings of 'persons concerned' were convened. Wainwright photocopied the paper to be discussed, issued it at the meeting where the first twenty minutes or half-hour were spent in silence making alterations or additions. Discussion followed, with Wainwright testy but capable, and then the altered sheets were collected and the professor and his setter stayed behind to decide on the definitive shape. If a meeting lasted more than two hours, Wainwright would close it and fix another time for its resumption. This almost invariably would be in the evening, and attendance was not obligatory; the setter, all guessed, would get his way.

The system worked well because people knew what to expect, would make sure that the setter understood their requirements so that discussion was only minimally necessary. Each setter paid particular attention to his colleagues' demands as it saved him time. Without exception they all mocked Wainwright's democracy, but it had about it a rough and ready fairness that seemed to date from some earlier, more energetic period of the professor's life. He himself rarely argued either about the content or the quality of the questions submitted. 'There's no need to establish your cleverness,' he'd instructed an ambitious assistant lecturer. 'We have acknowledged that by appointing you. We are assessing a student's ability to scribble down his ideas and knowledge under intolerable examination conditions. Don't make that any harder than it is, for God's sake.'

At the final meeting the professor flashed the papers one by one on to a screen, and each member could write a note of correction or demur. Most at this stage handed in blank sheets, or short lists of errata, spelling errors, misquotations, numbering mistakes, and these Wainwright consulted, used or not, then burnt. He had, it was acknowledged, no policy of deliberate mistakes.

This year Helen Southwell had called out about a passage of Anglo-Saxon set for translation. Usually there was uneasy muttering as the professor put sheet after sheet into his machine, asked if they had enough time, and hurried on to the next.

'That was set two years ago,' Helen said, strongly. The majority were taking a breather; very few students did the Old English option for finals.

'Is that so?' Wainwright looked blank. Dr Beatrice Bradley, the language expert, searched madly in her handbag, was called to order. 'Beatie?'

'You suggested the alteration,' Dr Bradley answered, still turning over the contents of her bag. 'You thought it a fairer passage, if my memory serves me properly.'

'But did it recently appear?'

'If Helen says so. I can't remember.'

'Then I will check.' He switched off his machine. 'These papers are not to be touched.' He spoke as to a class of nine-year-olds, and bundled himself out of the room. His absence stretched through ten boring minutes before he returned, puffing, with a box file.

'It is as Helen claims,' he pronounced.

'You specially asked for that passage,' Bradley said, voice high-pitched with anger.

'You might have pointed out that we had used it recently. You are the setter. It is your responsibility. Anyhow we must thank God that Helen kept her wits about her.'

Beatrice Bradley rose, clattered towards the door.

'Where are you going, Dr Bradley?' Wainwright inquired, distantly, politely.

'I am not staying here to be insulted.'

'Nobody is insulting you. The error is mine as much as yours. Please sit down.'

Bradley swayed by the door at this half-apology, but unexpectedly then thumped the panels with a swing of her handbag and made off. Wainwright blew out breath, returned to his machine, but offered no comment. The remainder of the meeting – little was left to do – passed with nothing untoward. As the professor was collecting his papers, he called out to Harrington, whom he kept waiting at his side until all the sheets were safely in an unmarked file, and the room clear of people.

'Would you go along to Beatie's study to see that she's all right?'

'Wouldn't it be better if one of the women. . . .'

'I'm asking you to go.' The sentence exploded. Wainwright's face swelling, red, veined.

'As you wish.'

'And let me know.' Snapped.

Dr Bradley sat at her desk, doing nothing, with papers scattered in front of her. 'Paul sent me,' Harrington said. 'He's worried.'

126

She lifted her face; strain showed as she poked at thin, untidy hair.

'There's no need. "I'm quite myself again." ' She twisted her lips into a vinegary smile. 'I shouldn't have raved off at the deep end as I did, but I had a beautiful verbal memory at one time, and now it's going. I resent it. I'm not much over fifty. I ought to have remembered we'd used that gobbet from Ælfric, but I didn't, and it annoyed me. And there he stands in his glory. I had set something else; he asked for the change. It annoyed me.'

'But you're all right?'

'Yes, Dr Harrington, I'm all right. I've said so. And then there was that Southwell girl showing off as usual. She'll do anything to impress men.'

'She. . . .'

'She could have made a note, and then Professor Wainwright and I would have sorted it out in private. But not she. She must call attention to herself.'

'I thought you and Helen were friends. You shared a room for long enough.'

'And got on each other's nerves. She complained to the professor, and that's why she moved in with you. I've nothing much against her, really, except her simpering ways and this insatiable desire to awaken male interest in her.'

'She's clever.'

'I shan't argue with you about that.' Bradley thinned her lips. 'She doesn't publish much.'

Harrington nodded, glumly.

'I'm to let Paul know that all's well, then?' he asked.

'Let him know what you like.'

'Beatrice.' She belonged to the generation which used surnames. 'I think he's genuinely worried.'

'It'll do him no harm. Oh, go and soft soap him, Dr Harrington. He's the head of department. You've your future to think of.' She relented, smiled witch-like. 'Tell him I've already selected another passage, which I'll let him have first thing in the morning. And forget what I said about Dr Southwell. She's a pretty little thing.'

127

Harrington let himself out, reported to Wainwright who had resumed his habitual torpor.

'An odd woman,' he offered, detaining Joe. 'Don't you think?'

'I think it probably upset her that she'd forgotten. She wants to be thought efficient.'

'The last word I'd apply to her.'

'She seems to have it in for Helen. That surprises me.'

'Nothing surprises me in this madhouse.' Wainwright set his chin in a Mussolini firmness. 'Well, thanks, Joe. We'll have to leave it there.' He pointed a finger. 'When you're head of department make sure that the examination system's properly run.'

'Not the teaching?' Harrington could not resist the taunt.

'If you can, if you can. But you've less control there. All you can do is see to it that they're at work on time. But as far as instruction's concerned, there are one or two here who'd do better to send in reading lists rather than make personal appearances. But I don't need to tell you this. But that's the present little imbroglio settled. I sometimes wish I earned my living as a solitary, a lighthouse keeper.'

Harrington burst out laughing at the incongruity and his professor beamed, began to hum, pottering about the room.

'To think, when I was your age, that I felt my life's ambition would be crowned if I got a chair. But it's no good telling you, Joe. You don't believe me, do you?'

'Not really.'

Wainwright tapped at the surface of his desk with his left hand, a blind man on an unfamiliar road.

13

Helen, arriving only ten minutes late on Saturday morning, thrust a huge bunch of daffodils into his arms.

'I'll help you arrange them after lunch,' she said, cheerfully. 'Drop them into a bucket for now.'

'A washtub.'

They laughed. He opened a bottle of dry sherry. The visit had begun propitiously.

All through the meal she praised his domesticity, comparing herself unfavourably with him.

'Oh, I'm quite capable,' he boasted.

'It's more than that, Joe. You have this beautiful house which you look after properly. I don't know how you do it. It's clean; it's cared for. And your garden's the same. I don't know how you find the time.'

'Shrubs, trees, machines. Everything labour-saving. A good man to help.'

'You must spend a fair amount of your spare time. . . .'

'And money.'

'I'm sure. But you get all your other commitments settled and out of the way. You're the most efficient man I ever met.'

'Helen. Let me make a confession.' The red wine encouraged him. He poured more for both. 'I'm content with the second-best. That's how it's done. You decide on a line of action and you carry it out. You don't do it perfectly. With houses, and gardens, I tell you, perfection's never possible. But you get it done. Or have somebody in to do it for you. That's where money counts. My father left me enough to splash about a bit.'

'But you do so much yourself.'

'At Cambridge I was unhappy, and only came to terms with it by working day and night. Six years' hard labour.

When I came up here with my marriage in smithereens, I settled for slavery again.

'Has it paid off?'

'I suppose so. I've come to terms with myself. I was a scarecrow in my first few months.'

'You didn't show it. You were very quiet and assured, putting us all in our place.'

'That's not what it felt like.'

'You're quite happy here now? The house hasn't bad associations?'

'No. This is my third year. I've bought myself out.'

'And you'll stay?'

'I'll have to leave if I want promotion. There's none going here.'

'I think Paul would make you senior lecturer if he could.'

Harrington did not argue; this conversation, maintaining formality, seemed affable enough, the chitter-chatter friendly members of staff exchanged with one another on the sidelines of some students' function. Helen sounded happy, compounding social ease with her anxiety to give him pleasure. After they had washed the dishes, they walked about the garden under the cold skies.

'I wish spring would hurry up,' she said, pointing to the daffodil shoots, the unopened crocuses, the thinness of snowdrops.

'Once we get a day or two of warmth they'll be away.'

'Like life.' But she smiled, made an ironical gesture of dissent with her hand. 'You suggested a walk, Joe. Had you anywhere in mind?'

'I thought of the woods out at Ravenshead. It's about, oh, fifteen minutes away by car.'

She considered it.

'I tell you what I'd really like.' Her voice rang bright, with force, matched her eyes. 'I'd just like another stroll about this district. It's a part of the town I don't know.'

'Perfect,' he answered. 'But we'll need scarves.'

After he had offered her a choice of neckwear, and she had taken a woollen in his college colours, he looked out a map

130

which he laid flat on the dining room table. He showed how the area had been a large private park; the squire had sold off three of four large strips on the periphery before the 1914–18 war for the well-to-do merchants or manufacturers to build their villas not too far from their places of business. Harrington's home was the smallest and the oldest. The family had lived in the Hall until the late twenties when they had sold off two more building plots, on one of which a son of the family, now long dead, had built a large bungalow. A large segment of the grounds was disposed of to a tobacco company and a textile manufacturer as sports arenas for employees. The eighteenth-century mansion, in poor condition, was demolished, though the stables, Victorian, had been remodelled as changing rooms.

'Do any of the family still live here?'

'Not that I know of. The bungalow's been bought by a surgeon.'

'It seems a pity.'

'I don't know. I guess that towards the end of their time here they weren't doing much in public life. Just worrying how to keep the place up.'

They let themselves out, and walking the lane inspected the gardens of the few spacious houses, playing fields and areas of woodland, all equally deserted.

'There's usually somebody out kicking footballs by this time on a Saturday,' he complained.

'Perhaps it's too cold. I wouldn't appear in my shorts in weather like this.'

Helen inquired about his neighbours; he dredged up for her what little he knew. The grounds for each house seemed over-large and secluded, but there existed, he thought, some sort of legal embargo on subdivision. 'I am very lucky with this place. My father nabbed it for next to nothing at the beginning of the war, and when he went back to London divided the ownership between my sister and myself and allowed her to move in. When she left I bought her out with some of the money father had left me. Financially it's all turned out very fortunately for me. Otherwise, you can see it would have been a bit above my means.'

'In an enclave for the very well-to-do?'

'Presumably.'

From the top of a hillock they could see in the distance the modern private housing, red-roofed bungalows, lines of town houses, detached family residences in crescents and closes.

'That would have spread over all the park, I guess, except for. . . .'

'Decent people live there,' she answered.

'Oh, yes. And some lawyer will do his stuff in time, and we'll all sell off at fancy profits to allow more of the decent in.'

Helen rearranged his heavy scarf quickly, tightly about her neck.

'It's interesting to hear you talk about property like this, Joe. I've never owned a house, not a whole house. What's its connection with what we teach? It seems another world, and yet it can't be. I know Shakespeare acquired land and a fine house.'

'If you make money you have to invest it somewhere. University lecturers don't make enough to acquire more than one respectable place.'

'You should see Paul's house. It looks as if he's only just moved in.'

'So you've said. Is it clean?'

'Fairly. But it all seems makeshift. Bits and pieces from sales.'

'Not a bad way of buying.'

'He's got no eye, Paul. His furniture is rubbish, and nothing matches.'

'But comfortable?'

'I wouldn't even say that.'

'He needs a good woman.' It spoke well for their rapport that he could come out with this, and that she smiled in return.

'I don't think he has any taste,' she said. 'His eye is absolutely defective. There are some people who can crowd a room

132

with all kinds of disparate objects and make a harmonious whole of it. You, for instance.'

'Thank you, ma'am.'

'Paul's a poor soul, Joe.'

'Aren't we all?'

'No, we're not. Even if we suppose that you and I aren't doing too well, we're not yet half way through our working lives. We've elbow room. Not Paul, though.'

'No.' They were walking now beside a hawthorn hedge, machine-mangled, grey, without promise of green.

'He said to me once,' Helen's voice, though quiet, had carrying power, 'that time rushed so quickly by him. He loved the spring, but whenever he saw the perfection of each daffodil, it dashed him. His own springs brought nothing new, whereas nature produced easy as kiss-my-hand these marvels.'

'It's in no hurry, this year,' he muttered, comforting her.

'He likes you, Joe.'

'Why's that?'

Helen flung back her head in the sharp wind.

'He sees you as he was as a young man. He wants you to make a name, and not give up as he has. "I'm trying to get Joe off this late-eighteenth-century tag." He said that again last week. "He's got all the headway he can out of that. He's written a good book, and some additionals. But now it's the moderns he should take up. That's what'll bring him advancement. And, best of all, he's up to it." He heard your lecture on Yeats to the staff wives. "Impressive," he said, "that boy understands what research is." '

'I wonder why he talks like this to you.'

'Because he means it,' Helen answered.

'I never trust him. He's so used to telling the v.c. and the registrar what they want to hear that he can't help himself now.'

She laughed, uncertainly, but did not argue.

They stood for a moment to watch a game of football through the wrought iron gate of the sports ground.

133

'They look so serious, puffing and blowing,' she said. 'As if they could kill one another.'

'I never saw much sense in games.'

'You look like a cricketer.'

'What's that like, then?'

'Slim and sharp.'

'No. Coordination wasn't good enough. Couldn't hit the ball, or catch it. I used to bowl a bit at school. Spinners.'

The pair moved on; the air cut cold about their ears. Helen swung her arms, and inquired about Anne Selby. Harrington, enjoying the chill among silver birch trees, gave her some account of Father Selby's last piece of writing. She seemed a little shocked, to judge by her silence, at his tactlessness in letting on about this, but their pleasure in striding it out did not diminish.

'We're almost in the country here,' she said.

'Yes, farmland and fields on the other side of the manor.'

'Can we see anything of the old house?'

'No. Grass. The old stone. That's all.'

'Was it badly built, then?'

'Or looked after.'

Now she ran ahead of him, whirling her arms, tripping once over a root and turning back to laugh. She had been released for some minutes, found freedom which did not include him and his preoccupations. She was herself, or a more innocent, childish self, unaware of the setbacks and boredoms which harassed her. Suddenly she sobered, sidled up to him.

'Beatie Bradley's sending me letters.'

'About the exam passage?'

'I suppose that's what started it, though it's not mentioned. She's adopting the pose of a candid friend, who's giving me advice for my own good.'

'What sort of advice?'

'Warning me not to make a fool of myself chasing or trying to impress men. She tells me a woman can have a thoroughly satisfactory and rounded life, without recourse to marriage.'

'Commonly argued by middle-class women these days.'

'But she's hardly the one to say so, is she?'

'She's like Wainwright. She knows she's nearly done for, that she was at her best years ago, and failed to take advantage of it. I guess we'll all reach that stage before we've done.'

He laughed, trying to make a job of his sentence. 'Before too long either.'

'Do you mean that, Joe?'

'We're all second class, but just clever enough to realize what the outstandingly good looks like, and to know that we've got nowhere near it. That's the irony for the likes of you and me. Do you reply to Bradley?'

'Certainly not.'

'How many times has she written?'

'Three.'

'And what's she like when you meet her on the corridors? Does she speak?'

'It hasn't happened.'

'Will you talk to her?'

'As if nothing had occurred. Or, at least, I'll try.'

She pulled a wry, little girl's face at him, not devoid of cheerfulness.

'Yes, I suppose that's sensible.' They were walking now down an avenue of trees; the path underfoot was overgrown. 'It's worrying. You don't know what she'll do next.'

'Such as?' Helen's voice cut icily.

'It's likely to be to herself. Though I suppose if she didn't make much headway with her letters to you, she might write to the v.c.'

'And what would happen?'

'You ought to know. You've been here longer than I have. He'd pass it on to the registrar, who'd either tell Wainwright to sort it out, or if he was particularly liverish send for you and Bradley, separately, try to frighten the daylights out of you and tell you to grow up.'

'He'd have no case against me.'

'I don't think that would hinder him. Mark you, he's more likely to pass it on to Wainwright who'd speak to you about

135

it, and say nothing to Bradley. I don't know. There aren't too many human beings working up there.'

Both laughed, not confidently.

Now they crossed a small bridge over a stream not more than a yard wide. Helen went down to the water, dipped her hand.

'That's cold,' she said.

'Yes,' he answered, superior. 'We'll turn back now.'

The two seemed more cheerful as they walked homewards, as if by their broken sentences they'd rid themselves of trouble.

'There's blue in the sky,' she said.

'That means frost.'

'Still, I'm pleased. And small clouds.'

He reached for her arm to smarten the pace. It took barely half the time of the outward journey to reach the road, where they clopped along. In the sports ground the footballers, redder of face and thigh, went at it as furiously as before. The ball sailed towards Helen's blue sky; the whistle shrieked; in the still air they could hear the voices: "Our ball, ref", "Mark that man, Tony." Boots thudded; breath smoked.

'I think there must be pleasure in playing.' Helen.

'I wouldn't be surprised.'

Helen put a hand on his arm.

'Joe, I've started my Spenser again.'

'Good for you.' He began to ask himself why she had only just raised the matter.

'On the early works.' Her completed chapters dealt with *The Faerie Queene*. 'I think they throw considerable light on the epic. I've quite a lot more to say about *The F.Q.* yet, but this will clear the palate.'

'That's good news, Helly.'

'Don't start cheering yet. I wasn't sure whether to tell you or not.'

'I'm delighted. I look forward to reading it. If you'll allow me.'

'It's not as far forward as all that, but I would like you to read it once it's somewhere near done. I've no idea whether

136

I'm writing sense or not. I work hard at it; it takes it out of me; I make myself put down nearly and clearly as I can what I'm thinking and feeling, but though sometimes I'm pleased with my insights,' she glanced modestly at him, 'I'm not sure whether, well, you would see any value there.'

'O come.'

'All ye faithful?'

They laughed, small sounds, together, then marched a few smart yards.

'Do your students make anything of Spenser?'

'Not really.' She frowned. 'I tell them it's a good examination topic, but they see it as a ragbag of childish fairy stories. They're willing to admit the moral purpose, but they think nobody grown-up would use Spenser's means. I tell them that their science fiction will sound just as unacceptable in a hundred years, but they smile. I hate it when they smirk, Joe, because they seem to be latching on to my own disclaimers, all the horrors I raise with myself and my job when I'm really depressed. They may not think Dickens has anything to say to them, but at least they can see he's talented. Spenser seems not so. I make them write a few of his stanzas to demonstrate to them how marvellous he is, but they can't do the job, and don't see why they should bother.'

'Sweet Spenser, moving through his clouded heaven
With the moon's beauty, and the moon's soft pace . . .'

he quoted.

' "I called him Brother, Englishman and Friend," ' she joined him. 'The key words are "clouded" or "soft" for them. They've no idea what's made such an impression on Wordsworth. They copy "poets' poet" out of the text book; it sounds right, they think, but they don't know what they mean by it.'

'They don't think any more highly of Wordsworth,' he grimaced.

'I don't suppose they do, though Pat Coombes – do you

know her? – came back to tell me how good "Tintern Abbey" was.'

' "Thee gentle Spenser softly led," ' he began.

'No.' A sharp word, loudly delivered, forbidding. 'You're as bad as they are.'

'Sorry, ma'am.' He pushed his hand into the crook of her elbow, but found her smiling, in no need of comfort, confident in spite of her nervousness, the spirit of the time, the stupidity of students, the unsupporting colleagues. She hummed to herself.

'How's your ex-wife?' she asked, not afraid of impertinence.

'Well, now.'

'Go on.' She seemed delighted.

'She's written me a letter. She makes out that the telly and the theatre give her no satisfaction, and this causes rows between her and her husband.'

'Do you think it does?'

'Oh, I wouldn't be surprised. It's contributory, at the least. She'll never be satisfied, with herself or anything else.'

'Why's that, Joe?'

'I've often asked myself. I don't know. Perhaps something to do with her upbringing. Her mother and father quarrelled over her, and she tried to do her best for both, which was impossible.'

'Are they still alive?'

'Oh, yes. They're not all that old. In their fifties.'

'And still living together?'

'Yes.'

'And quarrelling?'

'I've no idea. I didn't see much of them when I was married to Paulina. And nothing since.'

'Was she an only child?'

'No. The eldest. She's two brothers, one's in the City, the other's a dropout.'

'Do they keep in touch with their sister?'

'No. Or they didn't.'

'What about the dropout?'

'Barely mentioned, in my time. He got as far as university,

but left after a few weeks and joined some commune. He never wrote to his parents, or offered them any explanation that I know of. His tutor told them what little he knew. He'd got it from one of David's friends. The Streets made no effort to trace him.'

'Was all this a result of parental rows?'

'Maybe.'

They had now reached the bottom of Harrington's garden, and he scrabbled in his anorak pocket for the big key, which he waved in front of Helen's face. Once inside, he locked and bolted the gate, ostentatiously.

'That should keep the burglars out,' she said.

'Fort Knox.'

They did not loiter in the garden, but made their way quickly into the house which struck juicily warm.

'That's better,' he said. 'Take your coat off.'

'I ought to be going, Joe. I don't want to interrupt any more of your work.'

'You've some daffodils to arrange.'

'I'll do that.' She pulled her coat off. 'And then I'll go.'

She stayed, in fact, guiltily for tea, until he began to think, easily enough, that he was dodging work. They spoke very little, like a well-married couple, but the house seemed empty once she had slipped away.

14

Harrington returned T. H. Reeves's manuscript, and occupied not too unfriendly a half-hour with him. The man seemed embarrassed at his overweening pride in attempting to write literature, for once unaggressive. He asked a few questions such as, 'Shall I do it chronologically, or by instinct, a chapter that appeals to me?' Harrington thought he himself would use the first, though he saw the advantages of the second. 'You'd have more alterations, I guess. And you might be left with all the dull parts to write.' A crooked smile lit Reeves's face. 'I wouldn't include them, then. They always say it's as important to know what to miss out as what to put in.' He offered no new piece of writing so that Joe wondered whether this quietude meant that the man had lost interest. He hoped so.

Anne Selby immediately rang to say her father was delighted with the visit, that Harrington had really "gone out of his way", in her father's words, to be helpful.

'Is he still writing?' Joe asked.

'You have me there.'

Her husband was much improved, and mobile now, kept himself busy. The boys knocked about like nobody's business. She sometimes was fed up with the whole business, but had refused a full-time, nine to four, job because she didn't want to kill herself quite so soon. Anne laughed, full of high spirits. Yes, she would like some more apples if he had them. She'd come round.

Harrington received a surprise letter from Paulina. She had accepted the part of Lady Macbeth, had already begun work on it, but would like to talk to him about it. 'I'm curiously uncertain about this,' she wrote. 'I don't know whether I'm capable, but I've taken the advice you always gave, to accept the challenge, screw my courage to the sticking place. But it would be nice to talk to an academic about it so that I shan't make too many ghastly bloomers, and especially as Anthony Beaumont (the producer) doesn't seem to offer any advice as yet. "Feel it," he said, "and later we'll translate that into stage business." ' So, would he come up to London, or was she to visit him? She was his, with love, P.

He took the letter to show to Helen. Their relationship was warm; they supported each other, and she was still writing hard on Spenser.

'What on earth does she want you to tell her?'

'God knows.'

'I'd have thought that Lady Macbeth doesn't need interpretation. It's marvellously direct. Acting, yes. One needs a terrific range. Do you think she can do it?'

'Oh, yes. Tiger-woman, sleepwalker, the lot. Unless the rubbish she's been at lately has put the fire out.'

Helen shrugged, did not seem pleased.

In the lunch hour Harrington met Wainwright.

'The examinations are in at the printer's,' the professor said. 'All very satisfactory.'

'Beat Bradley has settled again?'

'She'll never be right. To tell you the truth, Joe,' he made beckoning signs for his assistant to approach, 'I'd be glad to get shot of her.'

'She won't go.'

'I don't suppose she will. Her little classes are all she lives for. And there's never anybody any good who does the Anglo-Saxon option.' He rubbed his hands together, noisy as sand-paper. 'Isn't it cold today?'

'In here?' Harrington asked. He had found his room hot and stuffy as a hospital.

'Yes. Even on these corridors. But I really meant outside.'

'When you retire you'll be able to spend your winters in a villa in Spain.'

Wainwright staggered, his face creasing with hurt. Joe did not know whether it was mention of retirement or Spain which had dealt the blow.

141

'I don't think so. No. Not at all. Good afternoon.'

The professor shuffled off, sighing, stroking his hair, wounded still. On his way up the stairs, Harrington met Dr Bradley descending.

'Is Professor Wainwright in his room?' she asked.

'Yes. I've just left him.'

'And what has he to say for himself?'

'He complained about the cold.'

Bradley eyed him warily, sniffed and angled herself down two steps and round him, keeping a big distance between them.

'Sometimes, Harrington,' she said, 'I think you're mad.' She squeaked, but softly. She had concluded he was keeping some secret from her.

'And what leads you to that conclusion?'

'You've got money, haven't you? A private income?' Her voice had resumed its dull normality. 'I wish I had. I wouldn't stay here with a set of colleagues. . . .'

She was already on her way, clipping down the marble steps like a young girl, but muttering.

Anne Selby rang him, invited herself over on Saturday afternoon when husband and children would be away at a football match. On the morning of the same day he received a letter from Paulina saying she'd come on Sunday. 'You will have had time to reread the play,' she wrote. 'I will call in after lunch, say two o'clock, so you needn't bother about food except for a sandwich. Ring me if this isn't possible.' Another weekend wasted, but he could see why she was in a hurry. He hoped to God she'd studied the play, because he had not thought about it, not opened the book.

He explained all this to Anne, who frowned as she strutted little steps of puzzlement.

'Is it difficult?' she asked.

'Technically. Not otherwise. But I'm not taking this seriously.'

'Why not? You should, you know. She depends on you.'

'She does not. Even if I had ideas, which I haven't, and

142

they were good, there's no telling she'd take a blind bit of notice of them.'

'Even if she rejects them, she will have taken them into account,' Anne pronounced.

'You don't know Paulina. She's clever enough, about the stage anyway, to be able to make her own mind up.'

'Then she's coming for some other reason?'

'Possible. But it's not likely to be an important matter. She's coming for the long car drive, or the lunch in my company or the chance to look at a different bit of the country.'

'She doesn't originate in this part of the world, then?'

'No. London. And Brighton. The effete South.'

'Like you.'

Anne began to grumble about husband and children, about the boredom of cleaning the house and preparing meals. Tony came home at differering times, often at short notice, and then complained about his food. He was due for an ulcer, she thought, but his worries were concentrated on his library and its branches, not on his family.

'Sometimes,' she spoke with her teeth clenched, 'I plot my revenge on him. I could kill him, honestly.' Yesterday he rang to say he'd have to go out with the head of Leisure Services. He came back at something after eleven and had been drinking. His wife had gone to bed. He had fried himself bacon and eggs so noisily she thought he'd waken the boys, and then staggering upstairs at midnight had tried to make love to her.

'He's so bloody clumsy,' she said. 'Like a bullock. There's no finesse about his approaches.'

'Why are you telling me this?' Harrington asked.

'Oh, you're on his side.'

'He can't very easily refuse to go out with his boss.'

'And why not?' She sipped the air bitterly. 'The reason I tell you is that if I don't tell somebody I'll burst and do something really desperate. You don't believe that, either, do you? All the sacrifice is on my side.'

'Is that true?' He argued against his better judgement,

'Wouldn't Tony prefer to sit working out problems on his computer, rather than answering daft questions from his assistants or the public? There's sacrifice in being a wage slave, you know.'

'I'm an unpaid slave.'

He said no more, remembering her crying-jag, her late arrival home. She asked to be shown round the garden. They muffled themselves and found few signs of spring in a place as colourless and icy as her life, but she seemed cheered to walk in the dryness of the plot, the chill.

'I don't love Tony,' she said, suddenly, under a brick wall, white-stained. 'In any sense.'

'Isn't that usual? Every day boredom and responsibilities knock the romance out of life. Or so I'm told.'

'Let's go inside.' She grabbed his arm to hurry him indoors. Once they were back in the kitchen she turned on him again. Her eyes, red-rimmed, seemed shifty, unable to return his glance; she reminded him now of her father, the enemy of the whole world. 'You're well away,' Anne continued. 'You have a satisfying job and a lovely house.'

'I don't think so.'

'You don't think what?'

She flung herself on his chest, arms about him. They still wore their outdoor clothes, scarves loosened but not doffed. With a kind of fever, she fastened her mouth on to his. When she drew back, he spoke.

'What's all this, then?'

'You don't think anything of me.' They still both had hands on the other. 'That's not true,' he answered. 'I think highly of you, and often.'

Anne moved into him again, kissing, murmuring her satisfaction.

'Take me,' she said, at length. 'Take me.'

He returned her kisses, then held her at arms' length. He spoke in a low whisper.

'We're a bit muffled up.' She did not open her eyes. 'To do anything too rash.'

Like a somnambulist she pulled her scarf loose, dropped it

144

to the floor, and began, with a careful slowness, to unbutton her anorak. That joined the scarf.

'Take your coat off,' she ordered. He complied, hanging it on a chair back.

Again she closed on him, rocked him with a ferocity. Her mouth slobbered, and she moaned. He stroked her gently, but his smoothly moving hands brought no calm; she pressed herself into him, wildly.

He attempted to unfasten the clasp of her slacks. At once she released him and her hands came sharp to her waist, brushing his aside, snatching the button and zip loose, dragging the garment down her legs. Her pale pink blouse now hung with squared ends, creased, exceedingly clean. She pushed at him, arms round his neck with such violence he staggered backwards, let her go, steadied himself on the table top, sat down on a chair. She stood over him, brought her mouth down again to his face, his master-mistress. He stroked her thigh and as he inserted a finger into her knickers, into the moist vagina she squeaked, sighed, resumed her assault on his lips. He pulled down her panties and she drew away again to kick loose shoes, slacks, underwear.

'A bed,' she groaned. 'Bed.'

They rocked together, she surprising him with her strength.

'Upstairs,' he ordered, breath short.

As he followed the naked buttocks upwards, he caught himself hesitating. On the landing he pointed at his bedroom. The place shone neat, furniture tidy, clothes away in wardrobe, duvet square. Anne rid herself of blouse and bra, and lay for him. He undressed without haste, and sat by her.

'Is this proper?' he asked. He could not have said whether the question was serious or comical. She answered with her arms, pulling him downwards, groaning, incapable of words. He took again to her lips, breasts, belly, genitals, great with his need and her stronger requirement.

In the end, twenty-five minutes later, they stretched side by side, touching at the naked hips, satisfied.

'Don't get cold,' he said. He felt tenderness towards her strong body.

'I shan't be here long enough,' she answered. 'I'll have to be getting back.' She leaned over to kiss his mouth, grinning. She seemed at home with adultery. 'Just nip downstairs and bring me my slacks and pants.' He brushed her navel with his lips; she pulled his hair and he slid, as bidden, from the bed.

'That was good,' he said, returning. 'Very good.'

'Yes. The way to spend Saturday afternoon.' She was examining her face in the wardrobe mirror. 'May I borrow your comb?' She dragged it into her hair while he dressed stealthily. 'I'll make myself decent now.' She thrust her nudity at him, but in immediate paradox took up her clothes, straightening them with deft movements.

'I don't want you to watch me dress,' she said, slowly almost sullenly. 'Go on downstairs, and make tea.' But she came across, held his head, kissed him dearly before pushing him away.

Downstairs they sat opposite each other, gripping their mugs.

'Don't look so worried,' Anne said, almost breezily. 'It's happened before; it'll happen again.'

Her cheerfulness seemed tasteless, as her clothed body smaller, less powerful.

'With you?'

'Don't start an inquest,' she ordered. Her self-assertiveness seemed out of key with the shy woman who apologized for her sons, who had sobbed herself sane in his house. This girl would have made her presence felt on either side of a market stall, brazened it out with the rough and toughest.

He drove her home, bag of apples on her knee. She wriggled from the car, thanked him for lift and fruit, waved, herself again. He did not drive off immediately, but stared at her front door.

15

Paulina arrived at noon that Sunday.

She looked tired, her skin putty coloured, but she seemed cheerful enough, describing the easy drive on a nearly empty motorway.

'Weren't you at the theatre last night?'

'Yes. And I did a matinée.'

'Aren't you worn out?'

'No more than usual.'

Her husband was in America and would remain there for another week, representing the government, 'at a fairly low level', on the question of export control. 'They send somebody sometimes whom they can trust and who's had connections with business.' She seemed amused; Edmond amongst the politicians. 'He thinks half of them are daft or obsessed. And the tame economists, well. He nearly spews or swears.'

Paulina enjoyed his roast beef and Yorkshire puddings, followed by a rice pudding, liberally sprinkled with sultanas.

'Do you have this every Sunday?' she asked.

'No. Poached eggs on toast. I've made an effort today.'

'But it's cooked superbly. Do you know I haven't had rice pudding since I was a child, and then I hated it. Yours is delicious. You never made it when we were married.'

'No. It's fattening.'

'You've noticed,' Paulina said, 'that I'm putting weight on?'

'No. I hadn't. It's not much.'

She pulled a wry face; she had refused second helpings and took neither sugar nor milk in her coffee. Harrington refused any help with the washing-up, made her stretch out on the big settee, covered her with a blanket. "Get forty winks in." She did not argue.

When he returned from the kitchen she was wide awake, eyes large, hands eloquent on the tartan blanket. Immediately he sat down, she questioned him.

'Am I to make a lot of her inability to kill Duncan because he resembled her father as he slept?'

'I'd think so. Because everything she says is said at the extreme. What you'll have to decide is whether or not it's a loud or soft extremity. And that depends to a large extent on your Macbeth. Do you shout or hiss? And when?'

They talked, swapping or capping quotations, and read at her behest a scene or two. She did not move from the settee, but her voice transformed her. It assumed powerful overtones, buffeted him like a box on the ear, spoke subtle evil or brazen conspiracy. Harrington enjoyed himself encouraging her quick intelligence coupled with so formidable a technique and equipment. They repeated scenes; at times he felt over-whelmed by this woman on his sofa. When they made errors, they laughed, but briefly; they had no intention except to interpret Shakespeare's mastery.

The clock, striking five, surprised them.

'Look at the time,' he said. 'I'll put the kettle on.'

'Sit down,' Lady Macbeth commanded. The voice softened to Paulina. 'You'd make a good actor in your little way. We haven't quite finished yet.' She now questioned him how she should react to Macbeth's secrecy about the murder of Banquo. 'I don't speak again in that scene, after his "Be innocent of the knowledge, dearest chuck," but I must do something.'

They took the scene to pieces.

'Nought's had, all's spent,
Where our desire is got without content,'

Harrington quoted. 'She seems to know what's what, morally. Depends, of course, how you define "safer". And she tries to comfort her husband by telling him to do what later she can't do herself.

148

'Things without all remedy
Should be without regard: what's done is done.'

The talk was quick, in new and old senses; Paulina butted in
with breathless energy while he tried to miss no word, to act
the Bradleyan judge. Finally she asked to 'dash through' the
sleepwalking scene. Here she combined guilt with a weirdness
of delivery, as if only sleep, the unconscious mind, could
expose her grasp of her evildoing. It impressed; Paulina Street
was no longer in this room, but walked, a gore-daubed queen,
in the darkness of cold castles, of the bloody past. Her voice
hardly rose above a whispering emptiness, but he was pinned
back by arrows of chill into his chair which forfeited all
comfort.

When Joe was finally released to make tea, he walked
uplifted, hummed, conducted himself, slid about the floor in
a small ecstasy of dance steps. Paulina had demonstrated her
talent, genius even. He remembered equivalent occasions
from their married life, but nothing quite to stir the spirit as
this had. He had been privileged to share those scenes with
an actress of rarest quality; both knew it, but he could not
understand why she had wanted his advice, his cues, his eye
on the text. It made a new man of him.

He toasted fattening 'pyclets', muffins to her, brought in
jam and honey, boiled ham and tongue, rich fruit cake, the
best that supermarkets could provide. Paulina walked round
the room looking at his pictures, one or two of which survived
from the flat; she smiled, said nothing out of the ordinary,
much at home. She ate, licking the butter from those capable
fingers, as if she celebrated a release.

'You've done me proud,' she admitted, fatly.

'Sainsbury's have.'

'No. I meant with the Shakespeare.'

'You don't need my help, as well you know. You were
magnificent. Still, I'm glad you came.'

'Don't underrate youself, Joe.'

'No fear of that, my flower.' He had heard the endearment
yesterday in the street, from a father to his child. Without

exaggeration, he praised her, made her understand the weight of her interpretation, its effect on him, until she sat straight in her chair, convinced, suspicious of no irony on his part.

'This has been worth a dozen rehearsals,' she admitted. 'I think I can despise Macbeth now, as well as love and admire him. It isn't easy.'

They talked easily about the play and its production, for she was certain of her skill. This time she helped with the dishes, after which they sat scorching their legs on his gas fire.

'I must relax now,' she said.

'Would you like a drink?' She accepted, strict about measures, a small gin and tonic, piled with ice. Paulina putting the drink untasted on the table beside her, said there was no hurry about her return. Nobody expected her; no rehearsals tomorrow meant that she must be on stage Monday at eight. 'More than twenty-four hours.' She purred. 'You've made yourself a cosy corner here, Joe.'

'Is that good?'

'I don't know. You won't tell me. Are you writing well?'

'I'm writing. Bits of humdrum decency. Fit for sixth-formers. Publishers love it.'

'You don't mean that, Joe.'

'Isn't there plenty to be said for setting young people on the right way?'

'Not for you. There are dozens, if not hundreds who can produce respectable primers. I expect more from you. Your first book was no child's guide.'

He shook his head, making mock of her seriousness.

'It nags at me,' Paulina continued, 'when I fool about with these television trivialities instead of Shakespeare. Edmond says it doesn't matter. Oh, he admits the principle that Chekhov is better than *Linda Laurie*, but . . . I think he looks on all theatre as unimportant.'

'You get on all right?' Harrington asked. 'His letter worried me.'

'I talk about you too often to him. He's jealous. He's a very possessive man, like an infant. I have to be so careful.'

150

'Not your style, eh?'

'He wouldn't like it if he knew I was here, unless he could come in and check on us. I shan't tell him too much about it.' She shook her head, rapidly. 'He's a good man in many ways, a big man, but he can annoy me, that I will confess.'

Several times she returned to the topics as they talked. Much at ease she stretched, in no hurry to go. Her drink was all but untouched. At nine o'clock he asked about supper.

'Black coffee, if you're making yourself a drink. Nothing else.' She sat straight. 'What time do you leave for the university?'

'Eight-thirty.'

'Could I stay the night?'

'Is that wise, in view of . . . ?'

She flapped her hands in pseudo-annoyance.

'You have it so comfortable here that it seems a shame to have to drive back in the dark. I don't like the motorway, especially at night.'

'Right, then. I'll make you a bed up.'

'Thanks, Joe. I don't often get a real rest without phone calls and interruption.'

'Won't Edmond be ringing you up?'

'He'll get no answer, won't he?' She wriggled herself more cosily into her chair. 'He'll think I'm at some party.'

'And that's acceptable?'

'In a way. It's part of theatrical life. He goes along with me if he can. He knows that adultery exists, and that if one wants to commit it, one can find time and place.'

Harrington wondered how many times she had strayed, but tramped his way upstairs to find sheets and blankets to make her a bed.

'That's comfortable,' he said, reappearing.

They talked again of *Macbeth*, and he expounded Libby's theory that Ross was the villain of the piece who had Cawdor executed on false charges, and as Third Murderer had killed Banquo, then slaughtered Macduff's wife and children, and to crown all changed sides and was made an earl for his trouble by Malcolm.

151

'I've never heard that before. Do you believe it?'

'No. It's unnecessary.'

'I'd better not tell Anthony. He'll want to use it.'

'Poor Ross.'

The theory delighted her; she kept returning to it as if the piece of literary ingenuity added colour or spice to her life.

'You'll come and see it, won't you?' she begged.

'I promise.'

'They're talking about filming it for television, but you've sworn your oath now.'

They laughed, pleased with each other, making unimportant confessions about their daily round, then swerving back to the play to clear some obscure corner. At eleven-thirty they went upstairs.

Outside his bedroom Paulina kissed him on the mouth, embracing him with strength, thanking him for a marvellous day. He resisted temptation, even warned, 'No sleepwalking now', but watched her enter her room with disappointment.

Next morning Paulina, unnaturally silent, ate her slice of toast and honey with glum speed and left at twenty past eight. She kissed him perfunctorily; even her sentences of thanks lacked plausibility. Without ceremony she stepped into her car, raised the left hand, sped away from him.

Joe, ungratified, stuffed unmarked essays into his briefcase.

16

There was, Harrington noted suspiciously, no word from the Selby family. He felt ashamed, though his anticipation of and excitement at Paulina's visit had hidden from him the full extent of his guilt, or rather the unrewarding nature of his act of adultery with Anne. The affair was not likely to continue; she was not interesting enough to him. She had used him to work off frustration and to slap her husband down, though he knew nothing of it. Moreover, Joe did not trust her, judging it would not be long before she let the cat out of the bag, boasted to Tony of her 'conquest'. He began to class her with her father, a cunning, unsatisfactory creature, whose whims were governed equally by past rebuffs and present self-sought discomforts. Worst, he could not see himself acting any differently had he been given another chance. She had thrown herself at him; he had been only too willing to reply in kind. Now he waited for judgement; some demand from her or Anthony making a second accusatory appearance, this time with chapter and verse.

His disappointment rankled.

He had acted badly, gaining nothing for Anne. With Kate Morris-Jones he'd known, at least he thought so now, exactly what he was about. Kate needed him from time to time, but made no public fuss about her requirement. With Eustacia Bates matters had been more complicated, but both were, legally, free. He wondered if their fornication had cost Stacey a job in the department, but he had no means of finding out. Had Paulina pushed last night he would have fallen into bed with his ex-wife without compunction and this bleak Monday morning the thought did not warm him. He read out a lecture on Blake he had written two years ago, barely understanding what he mouthed, trying desperately to concentrate without

153

success, though the students scribbled busily away. No one stopped him at the door with a question; the corridors on the way to his room were emptied as if to match the dull void of his existence. Helen made no sort of appearance, though she usually brightened the beginning of the week with her snippets of news.

On the way back from lunch Prof. Wainwright waited for him.

'Have you read any Christopher Fry?' he asked.

'Yes. *The Lady's Not for Burning.*'

'Was it good?'

'I didn't think so.' A memory jerked in him. 'We had a copy at home which my mother gave me to read one school holiday. She said, quite out of the blue, that it had excited my father. He'd said that it was most colourful.'

'Was he a keen theatre-goer?'

'My mother led him there regularly.'

'But he wasn't given to enthusiastic comments?'

'No.' Harrington answered slowly. 'He was shrewd, and he'd been there often enough to distinguish good acting from bad, but he always made his comments quietly. He could rip an opponent to pieces without raising his voice. I wasn't there on this occasion, but they'd bothered to buy a copy, and my mother who wasn't given to exaggeration without due reason said this, sounded quite excited herself and it made me remember it. I'd just complained I'd nothing to read, and she'd pulled the book off the shelves.'

'Have you read it since then?'

'Once. Some students at U.C.L. wanted to act it, asked me.'

'And you weren't impressed?'

'Not really. But I told *them* about my father's reaction.' He laughed. 'They called it off. Did a Tom Stoppard.'

'Fashion is odd, isn't it? I suppose we should be on our guard, but then we'd never opt for the new.'

'We?' Harrington asked.

'Oh, academics. Literature's our province now, isn't it? Nobody else wants it. Except those with subsidies to

154

distribute. It's sad. I blame the schools who don't teach their pupils to read anything like fluently.'

'Why did you ask me about this particular play?'

'Ah, yes. Ah.' Wainwright cleared his throat. 'Ah. It came into my head, I thought about it. Must have been in the late forties or early fifties I saw it, and I felt attracted. Eliot had moved to his prose-verse things like *The Cocktail Party*. That didn't suit me, somehow. And when I thought of this Fry play I said to myself I'd ask you about it, though I doubted if you'd read it.'

Harrington pulled a sour face but said nothing.

'You don't think it will last, then?' Wainwright pulled at his lapels. 'Not even as a literary curiosity?'

'No.' Sharp from Harrington. 'Though you never can tell. The human race is pretty gullible.'

Wainwright rubbed his chin.

'Would you mind just stepping into my room? You're not too busy, are you? There is one matter I'd like to raise with you.'

They walked the rest of the way unspeaking. Wainwright's feet hit the corridor floor like those of a man walking in shallow water. After the usual foolery with keys, annoying to Harrington, they were inside, where the professor moved a pile of letters, packets and parcels to allow his guest to sit down.

'Paper, paper,' he said. 'My life is stuffed with ill-written missives, and my equally worthless, I admit it, answers. Sit down now.' He himself moved ponderously round the desk. 'Will you . . ., do you mind checking that the door is locked? I don't want people bursting in. They're likely to, you know, without so much as a knock. Yes, just the Yale. Thank you.' Wainwright remained standing after Joe had resumed his seat. With arms down on his desk, he swayed, working himself up or towards some statement.

'It's about Helen Southwell again,' he said after a time. Joe crossed his legs, ready to hear about wild accusations in letters from Bradley. Now Wainwright was pursing his lips, nodding his head, standing with arms stiff as if his colleagues were not there to observe the oddity. 'You have not changed your mind about her?'

'In what way?'

' "Mind" is not the right word.' He bent now, stock still, relieved at his disclaimer. 'Emotionally is nearer. Yes. Emotionally.'

'No,' Harrington said.

'You do not love her?'

'No.' Harrington scowled. 'Why are you asking?'

Wainwright sat down hard.

'You know, there is no need for me to stress, that I think highly of the girl. Even there I use this flat phraseology to cover the depth of my feeling. It is more than mere attraction to cleverness. Intellectually, morally, physically she appeals to me. But you know this, don't you?'

'Yes. You've said as much,' Harrington mumbled when his senior waited for an answer.

'She would marry you tomorrow, given the opportunity.'

'I don't know about that.'

'Has she never confessed she loved you? Come on, man, be honest now.'

Wainwright's fists were bunched on his desk.

'Once. She said as much. It was some time ago. She may feel differently about it now. Love is a shifting, progressive matter.'

'Progressive. Matter. I suppose by that you mean she should have continued to say to you that she loved you. It's arrogant, on your part, and unlikely on hers. She is proud, and shy. Especially if you rebuffed her.'

Harrington made no answer. If Wainwright wanted to feed his spirit with such thin gruel, let him. It cost the listener nothing.

'I take it,' the professor continued, 'that you consider it none of my business.'

'No. Not at all.'

'What does that answer mean?'

'You are entitled to speak on Helen's behalf to me, or

anybody else, if you think it might do her good.' That sounded feeble enough.

'You don't believe it. You put it down to jealousy. I will go so far as to admit,' the words emerged singly now, stressed, compressed, 'it. I can't deny it.' He struggled to his feet. 'You could make that woman happy.'

'For how long?'

'If you did so for ten minutes it would be an improvement on your present performance. I know it's impossible to guess how passing time will. . . .' Wainwright broke off, ashamed perhaps, but then took up again in a more normal voice. 'You're out of your teens now; you've been married once. You've experience, sexual and social. You could learn, could teach yourself to cherish her. She's physically attractive, is she not?' He thrust out an accusatory finger, earning a nod from Harrington. 'And over and above that; I don't deny the pre-eminent position of sexual attraction in the first place; I put it first. Over and above that she is the most interesting woman in this university. Her mind is alpha class, and not in some limited field. Her capacity is not merely in literary scholarship or evaluation; it extends to human relationships, understanding of her place in the world, even, I would claim, *sub specie aeternitatis*. That's why she shines. You are, Joe, in some way, for some reason blind to this. If I could only open your eyes.'

Wainwright stopped, signalling with outspread palms for a reply.

'Nobody thinks more highly of Helen than I.' Joe shrugged his disapproval of the other's exaggeration.

'That's not good enough.'

'Not for what you are asking, no. You accuse me of blindness.'

'Is it not true? Why –'

'If I can say so,' Harrington interrupted, 'with respect, you speak . . . like a person infatuated.'

'Person,' Wainwright waved a feeble circle with his right arm, subsided into immobility. 'Has anyone ever told you,

157

Harrington, what sort of impression you give of yourself? What sort of a person you appear?'

'Often.' Harrington mixed cough with laugh.

'I doubt it. I doubt it very much indeed. You are far too pleased with yourself for your own good.'

'Possibly.'

'There you go. Holier than thou. Never losing your temper. Always above the conflict.'

'Isn't that an advantage?'

'Not so much as you think. People dislike you for it, look on you as bloodless, or uncaring. I do. You have no thought for Helen.'

'Listen.' Harrington reddened with anger.

'You will listen to me, if you don't mind, since I'm talking to you for your own good and not just for Helen's. Moreover, it is my duty to keep this department from becoming a depressed area, even when it means that sometimes I have to speak out like this, out of character.'

'Why pick on me?' Harrington spoke like a surly child.

'You know why.'

'Helen's making progress with her book.'

'So you say. I hope it is so. But there's more in life than producing books.'

'Tell that to your colleagues next time you're appointing a lecturer.'

'You'll want to leave us in due course, I take it.' Wainwright was now upright, immobile.

'Are you threatening me that you won't give me a favourable report?'

'Not at all.'

'Because if you are, my advice to you would be to see a doctor.' At the end of Joe's tight-lipped sentences, Wainwright smiled as if he'd thought of a good joke.

'I saw it as my duty to speak to you,' he said mildly.

' "I stumbled when I saw." '

Wainwright gave no inkling that he recognized the quotation. 'Thank you for listening to me,' he said. Harrington thought the man concerned himself elsewhere.

'My goodness, it's ten minutes past two.' The professor pointed dramatically to his watch. Harrington rose, and stood, not moving.

'Thank you,' Wainwright said again. 'Think about what I've said, Joe. It was meant in no inimical way.'

'You say so.' Harrington grumbled, walking from the room, shutting the door with a cautious quietness. Back in his room, he sat dizzily, unable to concentrate. Wainwright's attack did not frighten him (the man himself had allowed his anger to peter out before he'd completed his rebuke), but the accuracy of some of the accusations left Harrington numbed, even weak. He had let Helen down. As he reached out for a pile of undergraduate essays, Helen herself tiptoed into the room, smiling, telling him she thought he'd deserted them, as he'd been out the whole of the lunch hour.

'I was talking to Wainwright,' he answered, uncertain how much to tell her.

'About the letters?'

'Letters? Old Mother Bradley's?'

'Obviously you haven't. What was he telling you?'

'What a struggle it was to keep the department from becoming a depressed area.'

'You and I excepted.'

'Certainly you. "The most interesting woman in the university." Or was it "any university"? Anyhow you are in favour. So Bradders had better watch her step.'

'Oh, she's mad. But these are different letters.'

'Go on, then. Don't keep me on tenterhooks.' Joe kept his voice light.

'This is more serious.' Helen's smile had been wiped out. 'The mother of the boy he killed has been accusing him of dangerous driving, if not of deliberate murder.'

'But it was the child's fault, wasn't it? The inquest cleared Paul.'

'Yes. But she still writes these letters. He doesn't want to go to the police, or even his solicitor to stop her.'

'Does the woman's husband know anything about all this?'

'I think not.' Helen shook her head, pursing her lips. 'But

159

it's knocked Paul out badly. I'm amazed he's said nothing to you. I guessed that's where you were: with him.'

'When did he tell you?'

'Last week. Wednesday or Thursday. And he's had another this morning.'

'Have you seen it?'

'Not today's. He passed me on the corridor, and stopped for a minute. He looked really down. He showed me two last week. They were wild, and yet you could see that the woman believed what she wrote. It's set him back. His hands were shaking and he could barely talk. He kept biting his lower lip. I felt desperately sorry for him.'

'Yes. So do I. And yet he must know he's not to blame.'

'He knows it, but he can't feel it even without these accusations.'

Helen talked on for a few minutes, then snatched up a folder from her desk and left. She had comforted Wainwright with common sense or logic; very likely she was now on her way down to to see the professor again. Helen acted admirably; Harrington glanced at a short essay which presumed to explain why 'The Waste Land' was a great poem, not a piece of poetic grumbling. It was both, the student explained, but he had difficulty with the greatness. 'This poem expresses not the trouble of one man, ill, poor, at loggerheads with his wife, short of money and oppressed by the ever-present consciousness of loss in the recent war but the despair of a whole generation of western men, and in accomplishing this Eliot achieves literary merit. We are all touched by it.' Here endeth the lesson. 'Why,' Harrington queried in the margin, 'did so few recognize at first that the human condition was here given so powerful a literary form?' Harrington marked on carefully, pleased now with the students, who had listened to him, consulted the authorities, selected quotations with care; there'd be plenty of upper seconds this year. He wondered if they would read Eliot from choice after they'd gone down but could not decide. As he was on the penultimate script he heard a gentle knock at the door. Wainwright came in at his summons.

160

'I've come to apologize,' said the professor, 'for what I said. I had no right.'

Harrington stood up, still dazed from the biro-scrawled sentences.

'It doesn't do me any harm, to hear the truth about myself now and again.'

'I spoke out of my own misery, not because of your faults.'

'You weren't so far out.'

He held his hand forward to the professor, and they shook, not heartily, almost as if committing a social solecism; Harrington swayed with mild pleasure. Wainwright bumbled on, and escaped five minutes later, head down, hair tousled, like an awkward schoolboy without mention of the letters. Joe sensed a difference within himself, as he wondered what it had cost the professor to come up those three flights of stairs, when he never, *inter omnes constat*, visited his subordinates. He glanced at the clock: ten minutes to four. Helen, who was delivering a three o'clock lecture, would be back just after the hour. He settled to Eliot and cramped handwriting.

At four-twenty he completed his stint; Helen had not returned. He puzzled himself why Wainwright had made no mention of the letters from the bereaved mother. It put the man in a better light. Perhaps not. Helen returned, with a student to whom she lent a book and gently ushered away. Harrington straightened his pile of essays, and taking Helen in his arms kissed her mouth.

'What's that for?' she asked finally. She had made no attempt to struggle away.

'Put it down to Wainwright,' he said, and outlined his elation at the visit.

'We'll have to have him up again,' she replied, and scrubbed his hair with her fingers. 'You're as odd as he is, Joe.'

He did not argue, but when she had flung on her coat, hurriedly bundled books into a carrier bag, and quitted the room, he felt deserted. There ought to have been more to it than that.

17

Harrington invited Tony and Anne Selby over for dinner. He spoke on the telephone to the husband who passed him to the wife who named Saturday if she could find somebody to sit-in with the boys.

The host decided on a bachelor's hospitality: pork chops, greens, potatoes and a trifle. Large helpings would be the order of the evening with red wine. He considered asking Helen Southwell, but decided against it because she would want to help, and he preferred to work on his own. Moreover, he had wronged this couple and he foolishly half-expected they would quarrel with him before the night was out. Anne rang to confirm their acceptance, child-sitters organized, and spoke with enthusiasm that seemed out of place.

They arrived on time, dressed for the event. Anne wore a summer dress – 'I know it's warm in here' – while her husband sported a gigantic Iceland sweater in black and white – clashing with his multicoloured shirt.

Immediately they were in the house and had been provided with sherry in front of the lounge fire, the man began to talk. Tony had taken the boys to a local football match, which had proved ferociously hilarious. Twenty-two apes on the pitch would have performed more skilfully. In the final minutes one player broke his leg and another was knocked unconscious, and both were carted off by ambulance. The boys, wide-eyed, had enjoyed the drama; the captain of the winning team was the father of a schoolmate, and he had spoken briefly to them on his muddy way back to the pavilion, making their day. Tony seemed to be unable to decide whether the entertainment value of the match outweighed his sons' inability to judge or condemn or even recognize the low standard of expertise. He probably saw himself at fault.

Anne sat back rather distant and ladylike, ashamed of her husband's raciness. She smiled over her schooner at Harrington, who was genuinely amused though he had no interest in football. Once, however, they began the meal, she slowly, between mouthfuls it appeared, offered titbits about her father's progress with his autobiography. He'd shown it apparently, to some girl who worked on the local evening newspaper, and she was to 'prepare or edit' the early part of it into two or three articles on life in the twenties and thirties. Thomas Reeves was delighted; he'd share the credit with this Melanie Critchlow who, unlike Harrington, had a real interest in an account of a working class boy forging ahead in the secondary school. She had been to public school and Oxford and was working her passage, she claimed, into B.B.C. television.

'How old is she?' Tony asked his wife.

'Twenty-five. And very beautiful, or so Pa says. He's pleased as a dog with two tails.'

'It won't last,' Tony grumbled. 'His beginnings are always enthusiastic, but she'll blot her copybook before long. There's no pleasing him.'

'I'm thankful for small mercies.'

They quizzed Harrington about English studies at the university, and he found himself pleased to answer.

'We're very old-fashioned.'

'You mean Anglo-Saxon and the like?' Tony.

'Not really, though they all do a little, a very little in the first year. No, we have an agreed list of authors they will have to read during the three years.'

'Such as?'

'Shakespeare, and you'd be surprised how many have not done Shakespeare for 'A' level, Chaucer, Spenser, Donne, Milton, Pope, Johnson, Wordsworth, Coleridge, Byron, Shelley, Keats, Tennyson, Browning, Yeats, Eliot. And they're supposed to read round these. If you choose Pope, you're supposed to read Dryden, and if Wordsworth, then Blake. Then there's a tragedy paper in the final year; you can do drama each year if you wish amongst the options. We

163

work on the assumption that these are great minds speaking still to modern people about important matters. The novel counts here. You can choose that for each of your three years.'

'And contemporary writing?' Anne.

'Yes. That's an option, in the paper on the novel, or the one Poetry: 1880 to the present day.'

'What about structuralism, deconstruction?' Tony wanted to know.

'There's an optional course in the second year on modern literary theory.'

'Who takes it?'

'A chap called Clough. He's reader in the department.'

'What's he like?'

'He's clever, soon loses his students, and doesn't mind.'

'Does he believe what he's telling them?'

'He'll be accurate, as one can be. But I doubt if belief plays much part.'

'And do you choose books for them to read?' Anne.

'Oh, yes. If they do Dickens there'll be three or four of the novels named by us, on which there'll be specific questions. They're supposed to read the lot.'

'Do they?'

'There isn't time.'

'You named a great number of Romantic poets.'

'I know. My guess is that the prof., or his predecessor, or whoever it was who set up the syllabus, thought that students would respond most easily there.'

'Is that right?'

'I doubt it. I don't know. It may have been so at one time. We're always arguing about changes. But the kids are so ignorant nowadays I guess they'll find Keats as impenetrable as Pope.'

'I found at school,' Anne said, 'that it was the teacher rather than the book who made plays or novels acceptable.'

'There seems something radically wrong there,' Harrington answered, 'but it's so with us.'

The guests enjoyed themselves with reminiscence. Anne had been trying to read Ford Madox Ford and Scott Fitzgerald. She was sharp and amusing over the obstacles and exhilarations.

'They're entertainers,' her husband argued. 'You shouldn't find them difficult. It's not as if they were Joyce or Stein.' He clearly had never discussed this before with his wife, or realized what she was reading.

'Every good book makes its own difficulties.'

'Discuss, with reference to. . . .' her husband mocked, without malice.

They returned to the lounge saying they must be back by eleven, because Tony had to take the child minder home.

'One of my perks,' he said. 'She's nineteen, blonde and bustful.'

The other two did not join the man's laughter, nor comment. Tony knew nothing so far of his wife's adultery.

'She works in the library,' Selby said lugubriously, 'driving all the men mad.'

Once again, they led Harrington on to speak of his work. He talked about Helen's difficulties with Spenser, about Morris who belaboured Swift as an opponent of liberty and free speech, about the assistant lecturer who regularly condemned Clough's views on structuralism and deconstruction, but was not allowed by Wainwright to take any part in the course on modern theory.

'But won't he put his views in his own classes?' Tony asked.

'Of course. But he's appointed only for three years, so he won't step too far out of line. He needs his next job, and they're few and far between.'

'What's the professor think?'

'Nothing. He just checks that we're all suitably, temperately well-behaved.'

'And what about you?' Anne asked. 'Where do you stand?'

'Ah, that's it.' Harrington swigged his wine, waved the bottle round in invitation to the other two who shook their heads and covered their glasses. 'I'm a sort of Leavisite. A bit more up-to-date and receptive than the old man in his latter years, but believing that literature says something important about life that can be said in no other way.'

165

'And placing texts in order of merit?' Tony asked.

'Yes. Real academic. Shakespeare A, Milton A double-minus, question mark. . . .'

'But the structuralists won't have this, will they?'

'Those I know will. There may be some cracked hard cases who deny it. I see myself as one who examines language with the students as well as ideas, content. At a low sort of level it means explaining that "presently" in Shakespeare doesn't mean what it means now, and as most of our people haven't done Latin or Greek, have never looked at the Bible or a collection of classical myths, there's a fair amount of explanation of that sort going on, at least for a start. But some of our youngsters, for all my complaints, are clever and learn quickly, and by the time they've done three years are pretty adept at finding out what they're supposed to say in examinations.'

'And this is valuable, you think?' Tony.

'Damn my eyes, I do. They've learnt to read. A valuable training. They've read a fair amount by the time we've done with them.'

'They'll go on with this reading when they've left the university?' Anne asked.

'Yes. I'm not sure. At least, if they do, they'll be better prepared to do it properly. Three years of these valuable texts is something. And if they're introduced by somebody to the Marxist, feminist, socio-political, psychological or any other approach, then as long as they don't neglect the texts, it's all to the good.'

'What do these modernists look for?' Anne seemed wide-eyed.

'A thousand and one things. There's no accepted orthodoxy that I know of. But, for example, they'll look for assumptions that the writer may have held but was not consciously advocating, or even acknowledging.'

'Isn't that difficult?'

'All lit.crit. is difficult.'

'But you're searching for things that aren't deliberately

166

there. You can't be sure, can you? I mean, you might just be demonstrating your own cleverness.'

Harrington stretched out his hand to pat Anne's forearm. Tony beamed.

'That's always a temptation for us.'

'It must be exciting. When I was at college it was "What does it mean?" or "Retell the story" or "Give a character sketch of. . . ." '

'Do you argue these different viewpoints out between you?' Tony asked.

'Not a great deal. Never formally or officially. A few publish and so their views are known. But, no, we don't have public bust-ups in front of the students. The professor would object.' Harrington giggled.

'He sounds a wet blanket.' Tony again.

'So he is, but he'd be surprised to hear me say so. He sees himself as a liberal; open to all varieties of experience and their expression.'

'And he isn't?'

'He wouldn't want to annoy the Senate or the Council or the vice chancellor or the registrar. Or to get into the newspapers for what he considered scandalous reasons. He'd defend himself by claiming that the students need coaching for good degrees which will set them up for decent jobs, and it was not our duty to puzzle them more than was necessary or to lead them into views or behaviour readers of the *Telegraph* would reject. He takes the *Guardian*.'

'Not *The Times*?'

'He'll snatch a glimpse of the letter page every sixth week.'

'You don't much like him?' Anne, concluding, made the query.

'I do.'

'You don't approve?' Tony, with an academic's severe face.

'He's not going anywhere except the grave. I think I'd like a professor who was leading by example, who was still producing good research. Some of the science heads-of-department manage it, though it's always said that with them it's the young men who are more likely to make the

167

outstanding advances. I don't know. He wrote a good book thirty-odd years ago, and that was a development of a doctoral thesis. Perhaps he needs examiners breathing down his neck. He's done nothing much since.'

Harrington talked on; they questioned and he was surprised, delighted that his visitors found university teaching so fascinating. Anne wished she had gone to university and not training college while Tony thought literature would have suited him rather than the history and economics in which he'd taken his degree. Elated, Harrington compared their enthusiasm with his own and his colleagues' attitude to work; the students' grumbles, the postgraduate apathy or philistinism. When at eleven the Selby pair left, they said this was the liveliest evening out they had ever spent.

'I often imagined people having conversations like this,' Anne gushed, all teeth, 'but I never thought we should be taking part.'

'Great,' said Tony, soberest of three.

She kissed Harrington, flush on the mouth, then seized her husband's arm. The host accompanied them to the street, where handshakes and kisses were again exchanged. He strutted back into his house as one justified, lolled around with a final glass of wine, toasting himself.

Warm, leisured, humming Mozart, he picked up the unopened evening newspaper, cast his eye over its letters, comment and the announcement columns. Amongst the deaths stood insignificant, then sharp-black: Smith, Henry T. W., B.A., B.Sc. for many years schoolmaster and housemaster in London, beloved uncle of Francis and Selina Underwood. 'He fought the good fight.'

The single paragraph, amongst the three Smiths who figured, one with half a dozen tributes, sobered him at once, sickeningly. The evening's euphoria faded. He'd seen nothing of Smith since the day the Selby boys had marched into the garden to beg windfall apples. Harrington had intended to invite the old chap over again, but had always seemed too busy. They had not even exchanged Christmas cards. In these past four or five months Smith had, for all he knew, been ill, rushed to hospital, too feeble to lay down the law. Or his heart must have packed it in, unexpectedly, as he felt for his pipe or waddled up to bed. His house was unoccupied, the dusty books, furniture, tobacco jars all to be sold. No date was given for the funeral. The niece and her husband would know; he searched the paper again for the short, adulatory paragraph and found nothing. Nobody remembered the man. Even the relatives, in lapidary vein, were vague, not giving the name of the school where their uncle had served for nearly forty years, saving the expense of one measly line.

Smith had taught Harrington history in the third form, and for the occasional period of general studies in the sixth, but once he had learnt that he and the boy shared the same town of birth he'd come out with his ponderous schoolmasterly jokes about Beechnall, the fount of learning, or turning the relationship topsy-turvy would ask, when his pupil's answer was not up to standard, 'Can any good thing come out of Beechnall?'

Harrington had been surprised to run across the man first at a meeting of the Literary Society he was addressing at the instigation of Wainwright. Smith had remembered him; he did not forget holders of open scholarships, followed their Oxbridge results in the *Telegraph*, claimed to himself part of their success. 'Doctor Harrington.' He'd leaned at this first reunion on the title, but without irony, or precious little, and had asked at the lecture one of his corkscrew, simple questions to allow his former pupil scope for further dazzling scholarship. Harrington did not disappoint.

Now he was dead.

The man was good, but boring, otherwise Joe would have invited him back, but it seemed wholly wrong that Smith had chosen to die without preliminary notice. He had done his scholastic bit for forty years, and soon it would count for nothing.

Deconstructed, Harrington dragged himself to bed. By tomorrow he would have come to terms of a sort.

18

Easter, early in April, had not yet rid the year of cold, though daffodils flourished and the sun, from behind glass, struck warm. Harrington worked in the mornings at his books, spent the afternoons in the garden before cooking his main meal, and turned back to scholarship in the evening. The life suited him; nobody interrupted; he made progress. The Yeats was as good as finished, so that, in bed, he'd begin desultorily to read for his next publication.

Anne Selby rang to ask if she could call round on Saturday afternoon. He invited her, but with a sense of grievance.

She had dressed for the occasion in a smart, brand-new, sheepskin-lined coat, smart boots. She smiled broadly, shook his hand.

'I've been meaning to call you for over a week now. I've some news.'

'Good or bad?' He tried to match her brightness.

'That's what I want to find out.'

Her father, she blurted out, was going to remarry, the journalist girl who had helped with his articles.

'How old is he?'

'Sixty-eight. She's twenty-eight, a bit older than I thought.'

'And beautiful, you said.'

'Yes. In a frozen sort of way.'

'Your father isn't a very good catch for her, is he? I understood from you that she was ambitious, wanted London and the B.B.C.'

'That's what he told us. But they're engaged, ring and all. She's moved in with him.'

'Has it changed him?'

'Oh, yes. He bothers to shave, dresses better, cleans the house, cooks her meals.'

170

'That's good, then. He'll believe in Santa Claus next.'

'It won't last. I mean, how can it? There must be something wrong with her to choose a man forty years her senior.'

'Does she seem happy?'

'We see little of her. She works odd hours. But they came round for lunch, once, and once for an evening drink.' Anne tapped her magnificent front teeth with a fingernail. 'He acted more like her manager than her prospective husband, with schemes for this article, that broadcast, this play, that documentary. He looks younger and smarter, but it won't last.'

'Why not?'

'How can it, given his history and temperament? He's not said a word to my sister. They don't get on, but you'd think in view of his news he'd drop her a line, or phone. But not he. And he sneers at me, all very superior, "What about this, then, Mrs Knowall? You didn't expect this, did you?" '

Harrington made comforting noices. The news had made Anne more like her father than ever, shoddily cynical. He talked to her without hope or interest. In the end they drank a glass of sherry sadly together before he showed her round his garden. As she left, she kissed him and he pulled her into him.

'No,' she laughed. 'There's enough illicit sex in our family as it is.' He felt himself condemned with the rest of men.

Helen sent him two postcards from Greece, saying that she was well and thought retirement to one of the Aegean islands might suit her old age.

One sun-bright afternoon as he pottered in the front garden a voice hailed him from the gate where he saw two figures wearing identical fishermen's tweed hats. He recognized neither, male or female. The man ushered the girl forward on to the path and stood proud. Thomas Reeves, Anne's father, introduced his fiancée with an embarrassment of bonhomie. They just happened to be passing. Reeves punctuated his sentences with clearing of phlegm from a clogged throat.

The girl shook hands briskly, shifting nervously from foot to foot. Pale and pretty, a pimple disfigured the skin under her lower lip, made sorer perhaps by kissing the beloved's rough face. They refused to come indoors – Melanie had to be back at work shortly – but Reeves invited Harrington to lead them round the outside. He boasted to his girl, 'This is something like a garden. This is the real size to make something of.' He greeted Thomas, Harrington's gardener, with friendly condescension, congratulating him on the sunshine and Dr Harrington's wisdom of choice. Ted Thomas straightened his back briefly, but settled again to potato-planting without overmuch politeness. Reeves did not ape the squirearchy adequately, with his wheeze of a voice, but Melanie clung to his arm either in admiration or support. They left in a clatter to find her Volkswagen Beetle, after the girl had asked shyly if she could interview him about English teaching at the university.

'You didn't read English, then?'

'No. P.P.E.'

'Good?'

'I enjoyed it. It straightened me out a bit. Or at least I thought so at the time.'

'Useful for journalism.'

'As anything else.'

Reeves patted her proprietorially and said, 'You two'll get on. Know the ins and outs.'

He seemed to be undermining their characters, knocking their education, writing them off as a pair fit only to darken counsel with words.

Melanie Critchlow rang a day or two later to arrange an interview, was invited to lunch by Harrington who felt he deserved a day off. The girl arrived to his pleasure on time still wearing the tweed hat, her face still disfigured by the sore under her lips. She put down her bag, extracted a small tape recorder, set it up without fuss, tested his voice for volume and began. Obviously she had made some small study of the subject and began by asking what his students intended from the course, why they had chosen it, what they would go on to do when they left the university. The dust-up over structuralism at Cambridge was introduced and she wanted

172

to know where he stood, whether he had been affected by it, whether it would have long-term effects on English studies elsewhere in the country. Harrington asked her if her older colleagues had gone round quizzing dons what they thought of Eliot's pronouncements on Milton or Marvell. She said she had no idea, but imagined the media, especially the posh Sunday newspapers, had concentrated on it out of sympathy for friends or an understandable desire to stir the waters.

'Are you speaking for yourself?' he asked.

'Our readers wouldn't notice it.'

At the end of an hour they were briefly interrupted by a photographer. Harrington found himself pleased with the woman. She was bright without showing off, had a line she pursued but showed willingness to consider his disclaimers, to alter her views. She ate heartily at the cold lunch he provided, answering questions about the town, even mentioning Tom Reeves without prompting. But there was reticence about her; he wanted to know why an attractive young woman was set to marry a man forty years older than herself, but she volunteered nothing.

'Have you published Mr Reeves's articles yet?' he asked.

'Next week the first one comes out.'

'Is he excited?'

'In his slow, sly way.' She switched topics easily. 'He says you've saved his daughter's marriage.'

'How did I manage that?'

She looked almost angry for a moment.

'You talked to her and caught her interest when her husband was ill and driving her mad. You put yourself out, he claims, to give her something else to think about. That's what he believes.'

'I'm surprised. I didn't think he liked me.'

'He doesn't, particularly.' She closed her mouth, willing to say no more.

When Melanie had gone, he considered her again. She was less beautiful than she first appeared, too thin, too insubstantial; her attraction lay in the dark eyes, and the sharp, intelligent tongue. There must exist inside her some emotional

173

lacuna that made her wish to throw in her lot with Tom
Reeves. Try as he might he could not understand it. If Reeves
had been distinguished then some sheltered and admiring girl
might have cherished him as a husband, been honoured by
the association, but Melanie seemed shrewd, experienced,
wise in the ways of the world. It made no sense.

Once the holidays were over, he returned without
enthusiasm to teaching. He had spent some days of the
vacation in the library and his room, but his colleagues in
the English department were noticeably absent. Morris, with
open-necked shirt and corduroy trousers, had greeted him
once, unpleasantly, 'Glad to see you beavering away. Somebody's got to do it', but no one else. This term he hated in
spite of its lack of formal commitments; the students would
be nervous just before examinations; last year there had been
a suicide. Helen Southwell would be seen at her best, giving
advice about what to revise and what to leave unlearnt, but
to him, though he remembered his own furious preparations
at Cambridge, the finals here seemed distant, unimportant,
foggy. He did not much care about results; neither he nor his
colleagues, in his view, could make an assessment of any but
temporary worth. The scribble of his pupils represented little.
It was as if they had entered six or eight two-hundred metres
races, having practised only long, leisurely walks. He said as
much to Helen.

'You're down in the mouth, Joe. All university teachers
should go away at Easter. You work yourself into the ground
and then wonder why you can't raise any inclination to help
your pupils out, or even to try to understand what's wrong,
or right with them.'

'You've done nothing further to your book?'

'I allowed it to flit across my mind if the weather was poor.'

He felt irrationally angry, but shut his mouth. Helen, sun-
brown, cheerfully made off for her next assignment with some
nerve-shattered pupil.

A week into term the professor was taken ill during the
night and bundled into hospital. There he worried himself
more about the correct administration of the examinations,

174

it appeared, than about his own internal discomforts. The authorities moved him after a few days to a surgical ward where starvation accompanied X-ray photographs and ultrasonic scans. He did not complain, but begged visiting colleagues to see that his carefully arranged examination schedules were not disturbed. They promised, astonished at his scale of values, even in a few cases made an effort.

Helen came into their room one morning and addressed Harrington with a grey face.

'Paul's in a poor way.'

She stood, swaying. The professor had been operated on a few days previously, and had been sleepily unaware of visitors or of his own condition.

'How's that? Do you mean he looks worse, or do the doctors say so?'

'Both.'

'You mean he won't come out alive?'

'I didn't say that.'

'Look, Helly. Somebody of Paul's age, and not very fit at that, will look bloody awful after they've been digging about in his inside.'

'I suppose so. Is it cancer, do you think?'

'Nobody's said as much to me, but they wouldn't, would they? Why do you ask. Has he . . . ?'

'No. He hardly talks sense he's so low. He's not like himself. Somebody in his ward had died, and it upset him.'

'Helly, you're doing your best for him by trailing up there. What more can you do? He's in good hands.'

Tears ran suddenly and silently down her cheeks.

'Don't take it too badly, Hel. Tell you what. I'll go there with you tonight.'

She cheered up, fixed a time for their assignation, instructed him where to park. Briefly mopping her cheeks with a lace-edged handkerchief about two inches square she set off to face up to other people's trouble.

Wainwright greeted them with eloquent, low-pitched grumbles which he kept up during the hour they stayed. The operation, the doctors said, had been a success; the nurses

175

told him every day that his colour was coming back, but he felt just as weak. Yes, he was provided with meals, but he had no appetite; nothing tempted him. 'These young girls press the ice cream as if I was a child. I tell them I don't eat ice cream when I'm well, but there's no stopping them. They're very good to me, but they will keep on. "Paul, don't sit with your legs crossed." "Paul, you haven't finished your egg." '

'Are you in much pain?' Helen asked.

'Discomfort rather than pain proper.'

To rouse him Helen mentioned the examinations. Wainwright stirred himself to ask a question or two, but even this topic had lost its importance. Catheters and drips had wiped that anxiety out.

'He's not concerned about finals,' Helen said, trotting out along the corridors. 'I can hardly believe it.'

'He's in a different world.'

'Joe,' Helen touched his arm. 'Do you think he wants to live?'

'Yes. He'll want to keep a tight hold on what he's got.'

'Such as . . . ?'

'His chair, his committees, his exchanges with the vice chancellor and company, lectures abroad.'

'You don't think he has any religious proclivities?'

'You should know that better than I, and by the way you phrase your question I guess you think he hasn't.'

He pointed to a smallish Swiss-cheese plant, collapsed like a spider over its tub. 'Do not water', a notice warned.

'Is that Paul?' she said, half in earnest.

'Ugly, bent, bruised, but by no means dead.'

They held hands going down the lift, though Harrington was not sure why and swung along the windy paths together like lovers. Helen, brightness itself, chirped questions, pulled his leg when he admitted he'd probably work into the small hours once he was at home.

'You need a serious illness to make a human being of you.'

They kissed in the shadowy entrance to the car park. Harrington admitted to himself as he drove that Helen seemed to be the only woman in the world able to lift or shift his spirits. No operation, he thought, could alter her fineness. It cheered him to be able to make such a judgement, though he was sure that he could easily persuade himself that it was incorrect.

19

Tempers grew more ragged as the term progressed. Libraries were packed and students manoeuvred folders of scribbled-on note paper, clutched unread books to chests. They frowned as they shouted cheerful greetings, burnt midnight oil, cultivated rivalries, calculated chances hopelessly, took to beer or love as interludes.

Clough, in nominal charge of the department, rejoiced sarcastically, muttering innocently, 'They're working at last.' He invited Harrington and Helen Southwell to check the examination papers, to pack them into envelopes, stash them in a safe. This occupied a whole afternoon, which the three enjoyed, half-seriously mocking their own care.

Helen blossomed, big with solicitude, often seen in the company of red-eyed students. She reported a few of their sorrows to Harrington, but cheerfully, as if she were doing the right job, as if she could cure their ills. This succour qualified her to continue with Spenser, to complete the book. If she did not act as she did, she would be incapable of writing properly.

Harrington pooh-poohed the idea, though she went some way to convincing him. She wore brighter dresses, green, yellow and red tights, and on one sunny morning a straw hat decorated with a band and bow in her college colours.

'What do you think of this?' she pointed to her headgear.

'Jesus wept.'

She wiped her face clear of her disappointment, and he apologized, blaming life, indigestion, not her hat, for his judgement. Helen, at this time of year, could recover to save the souls or degrees of others.

Professor Wainwright was still in hospital, though now sufficiently recovered for the staff to exhort him to hobble round the corridors. The nurses liked him, laughingly instructing him to brush his hair or put his slippers on properly or uncross his legs. He enjoyed their rebukes, after the fashion of a knowing, naughty schoolboy. The mother of the boy killed in the accident sent him no more letters: his window ledge had eight choice get-well cards on it. Though he had half a dozen books in his locker he rarely opened them; he bought a *Guardian* once or twice a week, and talked with a free and easy bonhomie to his ward mates who could not make him out. When Clough went to consult him about some ambiguity in the administration of finals, he showed no interest, expressed his certainty about Clough's ability to manage, dismissed his colleague, but wrote next day saying exactly what he wanted done.

'I think he's quite enjoying himself,' Helen reported, 'because he knows when he's back at home he'll have meals to cook, cleaning to do, and he doesn't much like the idea.'

'You're not moving in to sort him out again?' Harrington.

'There'll be no need this time.' Helen was firm.

Harrington had heard nothing of Paulina, but twice Tony Selby rang up to complain about his father-in-law. The old man had given up football and his grandchildren, had accused Anne of 'spying' when she called in on him and had as good as ordered Tony from his house, for no reason. They had talked in a friendly manner for ten minutes, Anne had sent a cake, and then Reeves's face had soured and he'd said he'd no more time to waste. When Tony made no move, Reeves with thinned lips had spat, 'I'm telling you to go.' Tony had been so angry that he had snatched up the cake from the table and shouted, 'Why don't you learn politeness, you sour sod? I can well do without your company', and had taken himself and the cake back home. Anne had rung her father who had said, 'I don't want anything more to do with you, your husband, your brats or your sponge sandwiches.' 'That's ridiculous,' she'd begun, but Reeves had replaced his phone.

'Is your wife upset?' Harrington asked.

'More relieved, except that she's conscientious and feels she ought to keep an eye on him.'

179

'He's got his Melanie.'

'We wonder if that's not going wrong, and he's taking it out on us.'

Melanie produced her article about 'English at the University' with a picture of Harrington alert in front of bookshelves. She'd understood what he'd said, had read or questioned elsewhere, and had produced a half-page of sensible reporting. He did not think it would attract many readers, but the paper had plenty of room for one piece of well-written prose. He looked handsome in the photograph, and even the registrar commented favourably. 'You'll get us a good name if you're not careful, Harrington,' he'd said. 'Has Wainwright seen it? Or is he too ill to be praised?' He had chuckled drily at his own humour, as he made majestically off.

Clough crackled a sarcasm or two. 'Keeping us up to the mark, eh, Joe? By God, we need it,' but then turned serious.

'What do you think of Wainwright? Healthwise?'

'Healthwise?' Harrington scored occasionally off the other.

'Christ Jesus.' The man sounded desperate. 'He's having a rough time. Twice this year in hospital.' Harrington nodded. 'Do you expect to see him back?'

'I do.'

'It isn't cancer, is it? They're talking about his pancreas. Can that be cancerous?'

'Yes.' Clough would have looked it up. 'But he's not got cancer. The biopsy. . . .'

'I'm glad.'

Clough rubbed his hands, drily, vigorously. Now he would not have the trouble of applying for Wainwright's chair, knowing quite well the authorities would appoint somebody from outside.

'I began to wonder if he wanted to live.'

'Why do you say that?'

'One can only take so much punishment.'

'I don't for a minute think that Paul sees himself as a failure.'

'You've heard about these letters, have you? From the boy's mother?'

'I have.'

'He's showing them round pretty liberally,' Clough said. 'He asked me to keep mum about them.'

Harrington did not answer, ignoring the pun. Clough was not himself.

'It threw me, I can tell you. Our job, our claims for literature. These hysterical screeds, without the slightest verbal merit, terrified him. Frightened me, for that matter. As *King Lear* never could, nor *Oedipus*.'

'You'll be arguing with the students next, Jack.'

'Has anyone ever told you what a toffee-nosed bastard you are?'

'I'm sorry.' Harrington bit back his temper.

'It's all right. I thought you might understand.'

'Yes, but I don't like either talking about it, or listening to others reminding me.'

Clough shook his grey head, rasping the stubble on his face with fingertips, and glanced about, ready to slink off, rat-like. Finally he drove his hands deep and bunched into his trouser pockets, whistled tunelessly, twisted his face and withdrew, with an acquiescent smile.

Harrington was grave, moved heavily in the opposite direction. That was the second senior colleague he had annoyed so that both had levelled the same accusation at him. Not that that demonstrated any truth, merely that these fogies had discussed and agreed on the unfavourable judgement. He did not like it.

'I've annoyed Jackie Clough,' he told Helen Southwell.

'That's not difficult. His responsibility for us all is weighing on him.'

'Come home and have dinner with me.'

'I can't. I'm visiting Paul.'

'We'll go together.'

'I've loads of work. The kids will go spare if I don't help them out. This is one time of the year when I feel I'm not utterly useless.'

'Bring your stuff with you.'

'Joe, we hardly ever work together in this room.'

181

'That's because you choose the library.'

She yielded, grudgingly, in the end. He bought liver for a casserole on his early way back home. A winter meal for the spring. His spirits were bruised, not to be raised.

Wainwright grumbled through their fifty minutes with him, sprawling on his bed, lamenting the closure of convalescent homes. An old man sidled up to join them, mumbling that he would be dispatched to his flat and set a test; to boil a kettle and make a cup of tea. 'Then that's me over and done with.' 'Why don't you fail the test?' Harrington asked. The old man, affronted, muttered a garbled spell, tottered off, ash stick tapping, pyjama legs concertinaed. Wainwright made no objection to the interruption, listened to the tale he must have heard every day for the last fortnight, month, and appealed with his eyes and brows against the demise of institutions for those as yet only on the way to recovery. He talked for a little about Clough, dismissing him as no administrator who, though clever – extremely, even excessively, so –, would have failed as a head of department. 'He made a few applications, but I could never support him enthusiastically. Moreover, he's my sort of age, was at Oxford just a year or two below me.'

The professor spoke most fluently when he was complaining, but never for long. Interest or breath soon gave out. He attributed the success of his department to the fact that both students and teachers knew that there were 'thorough and strenuous' examinations at the end of each year. 'If you want to find out what people know, examine them. Similarly if you want to know what has been taught.'

Harrington left the ward thoroughly depressed, sorry now that he had asked Helen back. He drove fast deliberately to lose her, unable to bear her headlamps patiently bobbing into his mirror. She arrived not much more than two minutes later than he, and sniffed the air appreciatively.

'That smells good.'

'I hope so. You start work while I put the potatoes and greens on.'

Helen did exactly that. She settled at a side table he had

cleared in the dining room, and began to fill paper at an alarming rate. Twelve points about the Metaphysical poets, with the names of half a dozen poems to illustrate each. Every year without fail she did this, refusing to reprint last year's note in case she had changed her mind. Good, innocent Helen who knew as well as he that her students who begged for these literary crutches would forget three of her points, garble five, and present the others in exactly her words so that the external examiner might even suspect cribbing. Clever, sensitive Helen who should have been thoroughly engaged in her own work, writing as no one else could, would spend hours each day spelling out these basic points so that the dim, the idle, the tearful could scrape in among the lower seconds, and so satisfy themselves, their parents, their education committees. Harrington had argued with her often enough. 'If you must do the bloody things, do them once and for all, and print them out for the next twenty years.' She would have none of it. 'These mean,' she tapped the neat pages, 'that I am myself running through the topics I have taught, and this is to my advantage.' 'Are they so very different from last year's summaries?' he demanded. 'Sometimes, yes, they are.' 'Christ Jesus.' 'We are not all as confident as you, Joe.' She lacked judgement, he announced, because a scholar had not time for such conscientious foolery. 'I am as I am,' she replied. 'If I concentrated on my own research I wouldn't be able to do it properly because I'd feel I was cheating the students out of their rights.' He swore at her again, and she smiled as if she understood the frustration which led him to such vulgarity.

Both ate hungrily at the casserole; both took second helpings. When he was replete, and more cheerful, he instructed her to work while he washed up, but she refused.

'What did you say to annoy Clough?' She flapped her tea towel.

'Just suggested that he talked like the students.'

'Oh, ah. I can see that wouldn't be welcome.'

'I felt sorry afterwards and apologized because I think the man was genuinely concerned about Wainwright. He thought

183

Paul might die. And they're much of an age. If one goes, so might the other.'

'Did he say that?'

'No. I suppose he didn't. I deduced it.'

'Clough doesn't know,' Helen pronounced, 'when he's lucky. His wife is a beautiful woman who seems genuinely to care for him. He bought that big house of his years ago before prices became ridiculous; he's rid of his family and they're doing nicely. His trouble is that he's not lived up to what he considered his promise.'

'He's right in that. Cloughie's clever.' Harrington handled dishes with dexterity. 'Trouble is he's been too comfortable. And too satisfied with his comfort. His wife's wrapped him in cotton wool. He should have married a nagger.'

'Is that why you won't marry again?'

'Yes. Unless it's you.'

'Unless it's me what?' She laughed, grammar loose.

'That I marry.'

'Is this a proposal, sir?'

'If you like.'

'You Laodicean,' her lightness of tone matched his, 'you hooligan.'

'Well.'

'I never quite know when you're serious, Joe.'

'Neither do I.'

They continued their chore at the sink side in silence, unconfident, not sure of what they'd started. When the job was complete, he dismissed her to her revision notes while he dawdled over the coffee-making ritual. On his return she looked up, smiling, brisk, warm, at ease. There was no need for him to speak, but he did so.

'I meant what I said.' He had settled to one of the fire-side armchairs, having dispensed the coffee.

'Oh, yes.' She sobered her posture.

'I want to marry you.'

Long silence, uncomfortable, cold as winter dawn in the bright warmth of the room.

'What do you say?' he whispered, finally.

'I don't know what there is to say, Joe.'

'What does that mean?'

She seemed to tremble, then to hold herself stiffly against the weakness.

'You're not serious.'

'That's just what I'm trying to convince you that I am.'

'I'm older than you.' She plucked at her glasses. 'I'd have to start immediately on a family. It wouldn't do, Joe. I wouldn't want it.'

'I said nothing about children.'

'You're conventional enough in that way, aren't you? I don't hold it against you. Isn't it one of the reasons why you and Paulina split?'

'No. She upped and left me. We rarely spoke of a family. It never crossed my mind.'

'It must have crossed hers. You shouldn't marry another career woman.'

'Is that what you are?'

She started; her face set.

'You see. You don't even take me seriously in my work. How can I marry you?'

He did not argue this; it seemed too deeply unfair to be amenable to reason.

'The answer's "no", then?'

'There have been times when I would have accepted you, gladly. In delight. But now, this evening, you seem so devious and grudging that I don't. . . .' She stared helplessly at her finger ends. 'That seems ungrateful after you've looked after my creature comforts.'

'Will you think about it?'

'I shall do nothing else for weeks on end. Don't think I don't regard you highly. You'll be a success, and it's not spoiling you. Or not yet. Sometimes I love you so I can hardly bear to keep my hands off you. I dream my dreams, but they won't do for marriage. You know that's so.'

'I don't see it at all.'

'Well.' She pursed her lips, looked at her notes as if she'd suddenly been struck by some crucial, enlightening insight.

185

She poised her pencil to write, then allowed it to drop. 'I don't want to quarrel any more, Joe. I'm tired to death . . . I haven't been sleeping well. Please leave me alone.'

'If that's what you want.'

Harrington could hardly believe it; she wished him to rush her off her feet with argument or caress, but he did not dare put his view to the test. He would take her literally.

Courteously he offered her more coffee; she stared into her cup before she answered that she had not yet finished. He helped himself, stuck out his legs, bore the sluggish pain in his mind. Time passed. She interrupted the silence to ask for more coffee. He dragged himself together, stood, poured, returned the pot to the hearth. She thanked him.

'It's twenty past ten,' she burst out from behind her cup. 'I shall have to be getting back.'

'Yes,' he said, 'yes.'

But she did not move.

'I'm sorry about all this,' he said, recovering.

'You mustn't blame yourself. You weren't prepared, as Paul was. I don't know if that's good or bad. It slipped off your tongue.'

That angered him, but he answered pacifically.

'Let's forget it. For tonight, at least.'

Helen did not move, sat with her hands clasped in her lap, eyes down.

'Are you all right?' he asked, scared by this immobility. She nodded, slightly shifting her hands.

'I feel exhausted.'

'You can stay the night,' he answered, 'and save yourself the bother of driving back.'

She seemed to consider this, to scrutinize it for snags.

'No, thank you. It's very kind, but. . . .' The voice gave out.

'It's no trouble to me.'

'Think of the extra washing.'

'My machine's excellent. That's one thing I learnt from the father. He kept my mother really up-to-date. She used to make fun of him, but he'd list the advantages of the latest models. Of course, they weren't short of money. That made a difference. My mother always used to contend that the newer the model the less well-made it was, the more likely to break down. "They build in obsolescence just for you," she warned him, and he'd smile in his reasonable way and tell her he knew that, but that he was sufficiently wealthy to afford disadvantages. They never got cross. I think my mother really didn't mind, saw it as a way of showing affection on his part. As a result, I'm a washing machine fanatic.'

Helen smiled at the reminiscence, reading into it his apologies, then she pushed herself up. As soon as she was standing her face brightened, she became herself.

'I'd be glad if you'd stay.'

'No, thank you, Joe. I'm silly, but no.'

He led her out to the hall where he held her anorak. She zipped it close.

'I don't know what to say, Joe.'

'Don't say anything, then.'

'I don't understand you. Not one whit.'

She opened the door for herself, rattling at knob and Yale, while he stood away, the diffident servant. As he stepped forward she closed the heavy door; he had wanted to watch her progress to her car, but, typically, she had denied him.

Bafflement weighed him down. Certainly he had made a hash of his proposal, and she had pinpointed the reason for his failure: lack of preparation. One does not suggest marriage as the equivalent of a second cup of coffee or glass of wine. But the sudden change in her from a warmed and cosseted guest to a trembling, ice-cold woman made him suspect that she had some serious, basic flaw in her emotional make-up. She had become someone, something he did not know, not a ghost or zombie but a broken human being, incapable of fending off crisis, a woman he would not want to marry. Soon she had recovered, had gone off mildly embarrassed, loading him with the blame, misfitting socially but no more.

Staring at the two empty coffee cups he debated with himself whether her collapse had occurred only in his mind. Helen had not dropped into illogicality; her words made sense

187

of sorts, but the tone of voice, the set of shoulder, the tautened muscles of the face had presented this different, unknown, frightened, frightening woman. Such had been his interpretation; he could not now guarantee its correctness. Perhaps Helen had been knocked cruelly out of her wits by the trivial form and nature of his proposal. Here, she thought, was someone so confident sexually and socially that he could help along his evening's entertainment with tomfool offers of marriage.

Uncertain of the seriousness of his proposal, he began to blame himself. His behaviour had been indefensible, and he knew it. What he did not know, even now, was whether he wanted to marry Helen. He carted the coffeepot, the cups out, rinsed them, made his way up to bed, tired but, he feared, sleepless. He had acted badly. If he had loved her he could have switched from joking into an earnest profession, but he had not done so. Nor, he confessed to himself, had it been likely. Ashamed, he ran the bath.

20

A note from Paulina informed him that she had begun serious rehearsals of *Macbeth*, and that the company would do a week in Manchester, and one in Beechnall before opening in London. She said nothing about the production, merely gave the dates and hoped that he would 'turn out' to see it at the Theatre Royal. Not a word about visiting him. He booked a seat, and entered the event carefully in diaries, on his calendar, but did not reply to her.

A surprising letter arrived from Anne Selby announcing that her father's engagement to Melanie Critchlow was over. The information was baldly conveyed so that he did not know how she had learnt of the break-up. He gathered that she had not seen her father and intended to keep out of his way. She wrote this just in case Reeves approached Harrington, not very likely he thought, and then he'd have time to consider his advice. This was only what she had expected, but she could not guess what the effect on her father would be. She, Tony and the boys were all well. She was his sincerely.

Wainwright was now out of hospital, but unfit as yet for work. He could hobble down to the paper shop or post office, but not drive his car. Clough drove him up to the university one afternoon, where the professor stared about him, shook hands with those who went down to his room, not Harrington who had the day free, but according to report evinced no more than a stranger's interest. He spoke to students who spoke to him, but clearly regarded this academic existence as of no importance compared with his own last weeks of illness. They, he said as much to Clough who reported it to colleagues with evil glee, merely read words; he had outfaced death.

Helen Southwell and Harrington were polite with each other. At first he had expected her to mention his proposal

189

at every meeting just as he had imagined that on his desk the morning after he would find a written explanation of her behaviour, but she neither spoke nor wrote about the evening in his house. This did not please him; he felt uncomfortable in her company while she acted at ease. Disadvantaged he smiled, listened, helped her once to carry an awkward parcel of books and hated the dim relationship. When he asked if she had moved in again with the professor, she coolly answered, 'Of course I haven't', but admitted she called in most days and did the old man's laundry for him.

Anne Selby fell in with expectations.

She phoned and asked to be allowed to call. On an afternoon of rain, sunshine, white clouds she looked young and pretty in her waterproof, green coat and hat. She confessed to be worried about her father, but admitted she had not attempted to get in touch with him.

'What does Tony say?'

'He's sorry for him. He didn't say much to me, because he's not looking for trouble, but I think he was quite proud of dad's shacking up with a dolly bird.'

'*Ipsissima verba?*'

'I beg your pardon?'

'Are they his own words? "Dolly bird", "shack up"?'

'Yes.' She looked offended.

'Well, tell me what you think now.'

Anne drew herself together, shrugging.

'You know that he and I don't get on,' she began. 'I try to make allowances for the rough time he had as a prisoner of war, but even so there's no real excuse. My sister's the same. She never even writes to him now let alone comes to see him. We could do nothing right, at school, at home, with boyfriends, girlfriends, the lot. And when my mother left him, and us – I was a teenager, we were still both at school, Sal and I – we sided with her. Again, we couldn't say much. We hardly dared.'

'Why didn't you go with your mother?'

'No opportunity. Perhaps she thought we could or might look after him. I've often wondered. First off, she'd no settled

190

place, or she didn't want to interrupt our education. I don't know. But you can imagine the effect on him. Here was the world turning against him again, and he took his ill temper out on us. Sally, my sister, used to say she wouldn't raise a finger to help him if she found him lying in the gutter. She'd look forward to it.'

'Was he unpopular at his school?'

'He could be very sarcastic, and they were frightened of him, but he was a very good football coach. His teams won no end of cups and medals. Several of his boys became professionals.'

'And this latest thing? This Melanie business?'

'He said nothing to us for a start. And it seemed to develop like wildfire. He sent a piece of writing to her, and she called in on him.'

'What did you think of her?'

'We hardly saw anything of her. He kept her as far away from us as he could. He thought, perhaps, he was making a fool of himself. But you met her. How did you find her?'

'Very sensible,' Harrington answered. 'She asked the right questions, and could interpret my answers without too much trouble.'

'You liked her?'

'It wasn't a question of liking. She did her job pleasantly and efficiently. If you're wondering if I picked up any clues why she should want to marry a man forty years older than she was, the answer is: I didn't. She seemed normal, ordinary to me.' He watched Anne, who nodded, suspecting him as part of the male conspiracy. 'How did you find out they'd split?'

'She rang me one evening. Said she ought to let me know.'

'Did she sound upset?'

'It's hard to say. I tried to get out of her all I could, whether they'd rowed, and about what, but she wasn't having any of it. "It wasn't working out," she said, but she felt enough for him to realize how horrible it was to be left on his own, and so she was warning me.'

'Warning?'

191

'Telling me, then. She was a bit cheeky with it, I thought, because she said outright that she knew I didn't get on with him. I didn't like it and told her that if she thought as highly of him as all that, she'd hang on to him and not pester me with her discards.'

'And?'

'She didn't lose her wool. I'll give her credit. It just wasn't going to work out, and so they'd split up. She felt bound to let me know, and now I could do as I liked. I thanked her, sarcastically, and she put the phone down.'

'And you haven't been to see him?'

'No. Should I?'

Harrington read defiance in her attitude, as if she expected him to admonish her. She stood ready with her answers, and her sturdy prettiness showed it.

'He's not going to make my life hell again,' she said. 'He did it for long enough and I learnt my lesson.'

So parents direct your life while you're young, when you have no chance, or resources, to object or fight back. He half-pondered the truth of that. Was the university English department shaped years ago by an ignorant miscellany of fathers and mothers? It seemed unlikely; his colleagues' backgrounds went generally unmentioned. His own father, rather elderly, in years and ways, had been mildly, distantly encouraging, while his mother was both strict in her beliefs, but easy on him. Alicia, his sister, ten years older than he, had done more than they to form his character until she married and slipped out of his life. His parents, colourless as they may have been, had left him nicely off when they died. That was sensible of them at least. It showed forethought.

Wainwright's father had been a well-to-do wholesale grocer, and that perhaps accounted for the professor's obsession with examinations, the thorough stocktaking at the end of the year. Helen's father had been a headmaster who had died soon after she had taken her degree; her mother and older, unmarried sister were both teachers, who lived in a bungalow in Kent, full of books and records; both women were proud of the clever member of their family, the D.Phil., had done their

192

all to encourage her. Clough's father had been a minor civil servant; his mother still lived alone, vigorously, in her nineties. Morris, the only one from the working class, had a father who had been made redundant as a labourer at the ironworks; his brother managed a Co-op superstore. Little was said of his sisters, married to a clerk, a postman and a builder, nor of his mother, now dead. Harrington wished he knew something of her; though he had never learnt her first name, she must have been a remarkable, if limited, woman. How did he deduce that? From the character of her son? Harrington gave up his genealogical imaginings to turn back to Anne Selby.

'I'm just telling you,' she said, forthrightly, 'in case he comes polling round here.'

'Very good.'

She left soon after, apparently pleased with herself even as she expressed her uncertainty about her father.

'He's not suicidal?' Harrington asked.

'Why should you say that?' Her face showed shock.

'He hasn't tried . . . before . . . has he?'

Anne shook her head, replaced, shaped the attractive green hat, and fairly scuttled away. Harrington had not done well. Again. He looked out at the massing white clouds, spring-full, Lawrentian, more suitable to March than early May, and hoped for a bright summer. He hated the forthcoming examination period, but as soon as term ended he would fly to Athens, soak himself in sunshine before he came back here to work, to start his booklet on Romanticism, potter about his estate, harvest with enjoyment his peas and runner beans, live the life of Riley until October, master of his fate. The wind rattled windowpanes; a burst of sunshine flared and was gone; he expected a spatter of rain spots but saw none.

That evening the second of Reeves's articles, 'School in the Twenties and Thirties', appeared in the local newspaper. It occupied a whole page, was well-written and two photographs of lines of jerseyed and pinafored pupils illustrated it. The by-line read: Thomas Reeves and Melanie Critchlow. She had taken some of the pseudo-literary flavour from Reeves's sentences so that it now read interestingly, easily. Melanie, whatever her faults, knew her job, and Harrington wondered whether she had, or how, won her collaborator's agreement to her alterations, or merely changed without preliminary negotiation.

Reeves rang him testily at 10.30 p.m. to ask if he'd seen the article.

'Yes, I read them both.'

'What did you think?'

'Interesting. Really well done.'

A pause. He could hear Reeves breathing.

'She's left me. She's gone. Did you know?'

'Melanie?'

'Yes. Hasn't our Anne said anything?'

'I'm sorry.'

'Sorry? Isn't it what you expected? Nearly forty years difference between us. It wasn't sensible.' Harrington hugged his silence. 'Well, it wasn't, was it?' Reeves's voice snapped angrily. 'You might as well admit it. You're not very forthcoming are you? I shall have to grin and abide.'

'Yes. If you can.'

'Can. Of course I bloody can. I knew it wouldn't last. How could it? I'm not that deranged.'

'Will you continue to collaborate on your reminiscences?'

'Well, do you know?, that wasn't one of the subjects touched on when we parted.' Sarcasm rasped. 'I don't know. I don't much care. What did you think of her?'

'Very efficient.'

'Not the word I'd choose.' Harrington wondered if the old man was sober. 'Still, sod her, I say.' More heavy breathing. 'Do you see anything of our Anne?'

'Very infrequently.'

'She'll tell you all about it.'

'Does she know?' Harrington asked, smoothly lying.

'I never thought about that. I expect so. She's got her sharp nose into everything.'

'You haven't told her?'

194

'I've told her nothing. I've not seen her. Last time I saw that husband of hers I ordered him out of my house.'

Again Harrington did not comment; the two men stood, instruments upraised like weapons.

'Well, thanks for your call. I must ring off now. I've some reading to do.'

'At this time of night?'

'Afraid so. I'm sorry about your news. I was looking forward to more of your memoirs. Good night, Mr Reeves, and thank you.'

Harrington put down the phone, imagining the other man left stranded staring into the mouthpiece as if it had bitten him. He deplored his brusqueness, but Reeves was not to be comforted.

First thing in the morning of the next day he found Helen at her desk opening letters. She seemed cheerful, had been invited to review a new book on Skelton and to act as an examiner for a Ph.D. at Hull.

'I ought to have invited you to go with me to see Paulina's *Macbeth*,' he said.

'I've a ticket already. For the first night. I'm going with Irene Snow.' She smiled broadly. 'Anyway, you wouldn't want me there. You'll want to talk to Paulina afterwards.'

'You don't fancy seeing it twice? I'm going on Wednesday. That's if I can get you a ticket.'

She fiddled in her bag for a diary, opened it, both nervously and soberly.

'I'm not doing anything that evening. But you don't want. . . .'

'I'll ring the box office as soon as they open.'

'But are you sure, Joe? I mean, you'll want. . . .'

She gathered her mail together, walked out uncoordinated as old Bradley. Later that morning he arranged the booking.

In the afternoon coming from a revision seminar on Pope he met Wainwright in the corridor. He suspected the professor of skulking in wait for him, but bundled into inquiries about the old man's health.

'Improving. Slowly, slowly.' Wainwright looked paler,

195

thinner and seemed to prop himself on a banister. His voice was husky.

'You're not back yet? For good?'

'No, no, no. Still on what they called in my boyhood "the club". I'll be looking in from time to time. I lack strength, Joe, mustn't overdo it.'

Wainwright talked on, dazed. Harrington invited him upstairs to his room for a cup of coffee.

'Thank you. Climbing up and down these stairs will do me good.'

The professor sat on Helen's chair, staring into his mug, shaking the liquid as if to hypnotize himself. His wrists were thin, his hands dead and fleshless, his knees bony under smart trousers. Clearly he found no comfort sitting, wriggled, sighed, groaned. In the end he shook a finger, not at his subordinate, but at the wall, warning himself.

'I tell you one thing I've learnt.' He spoke earnestly. 'Since I came out of hospital.' Now he looked for Harrington's attention. 'The world appears exactly the same whether I'm here or not. I don't just mean the houses or the trees in the gardens. The men go to work and the children to school at the same time that they always did. And so they would if I had died.' His voice strengthened. 'In the same cars and suits, the same expression on their faces. My presence or absence makes no difference to the world.'

'That's to be expected, isn't it?'

'Not by me. I'm no solipsist. I don't create the world. But I thought I made some slight impression on it.'

'So you do,' Harrington assured him.

'And it's much the same with the department,' Wainwright continued, ignoring the assurance. 'It hasn't collapsed in my absence. The students are taught and looked after. But perhaps I can take some slight credit for that. What do you think?'

'I'm sure that's so.' Harrington felt sorry for the man.

'My appointments have never veered towards the extreme and that has led some to accuse me of mediocrity. I like clever people, and you'd be surprised how many who have applied could not be called intelligent on any count, and I look for those who are assiduous, but not those who think their teaching of literature will put the world to rights. I do not want fanatics.'

'Not one?' Harrington asked, amused.

'Not one. Radical damage is caused by ones. I've nothing against new subjects or new approaches; I like enthusiasm, but. . . . So you see my principle. And I think it has worked out. We get every year a large field of well-qualified students, who are looked after, and who go out to interesting and lucrative posts. And this makes a difference to the way the department is regarded internally, here, in the university. We have been fortunate, even in these days of savage retrenchment. Other professors have fared less well, staff-wise. We're on an even keel. You should think about these matters, Joe, because one of these days you will become a head of department who needs to know what he expects of his colleagues. That is one reason why I have tried to shunt you towards twentieth-century studies. The eighteenth century is a dead end in the promotion race if that is all you have to offer.'

Wainwright sighed as if the speech had exhausted him; Harrington grinned, amused at the self-deception. The professor, having swilled down his coffee, rose stiffly to his feet, balancing awkwardly with one hand splayed on Helen's desk.

'I've enjoyed our talk, Joe. Thank you for your hospitality.'

He staggered forward, groaning aloud, but raised a hand before he closed the door. Illness had fined his body down, but his misconceptions remained.

Harrington collected the mugs, washed them spotless, turned to William Butler Yeats.

21

Anne Selby phoned for an appointment, and appeared with a cake. Summer was making progress in the sky above Harrington's garden.

'Have you been in touch with your father?' he asked.

'Yes. Worse luck.'

'He's surviving, is he?'

'So he said. I rang him, and he asked me what the hell I wanted. Then he accused me of malicious curiosity. It quietened him for a minute or two when I told him that Melanie had been in touch with me. But he'd no time for gossip. He didn't particularly want to see me, or that "long streak of piss", Tony. The longer he talked, the nastier he sounded. I just said I'd ring again.'

'And you haven't been round?'

'No. I phoned my sister and gave her the details. Her view was "Serve him right". She won't send him a birthday card, either, next month, but I might have expected it. She really is bitter.'

'As you're not.'

She shook her head, praised Tony, said how well the boys were doing at school. Things flourished in the Selby household so that she would do her father a good turn if it were possible. She inquired about Harrington's work; university topics attracted her. She pressed him for information; her voice rang bright and interested as it did not when she discussed her father. As usual, she did not outstay her welcome, marched smartly off after forty minutes to pick up the boys from school, refusing a lift in his car. She seemed sturdy, integrated of personality, seeing the way ahead, this woman who had sobbed with violence, who had flung herself at him in adultery.

198

A week later Harrington met Reeves in the street.

'You're out of your way, aren't you?'

Reeves waved his walking stick, a new acquisition, and said he had plenty of time on his hands to examine the highways and byways.

'And how are you keeping?'

'Since that Melanie bitch left me? Untouched by it all. Enjoying my bit of solitude.'

'Good.'

'You don't believe it, do you?'

'I shall have to.'

Reeves rapped the pavement with the brazen ferrule of his stick.

'I expect nothing from anybody. That's the safest philosophy for an old man. It's no use trying to buy affection. Well, not now. For me. It's too late.'

'Does your daughter visit you?'

'Neither of them. Anne will give me a ring on the blower if the mood takes her, but I tell you I don't expect much from that quarter.'

'I'm sorry.'

'Sorry. It's what you should expect. It's natural. Do you put yourself out to see your parents?'

'They're both dead.'

'What was it Sophocles wrote?' Reeves waited impatiently. 'Come on. You're the professor of literature.' He rapped with his stick.

'Thy portion esteem I highest
Who wast not ever begot;
Thine next, being born who diest
And straightway again art not.

Dead. That's best.' Reeves having caught his companion out on a literary matter seemed cheerful.

'Housman's version,' Harrington said.

'Very likely.' Reeves set his shoulders. 'Very likely. Well, keep your nose clean.'

He swaggered off.

A day or two later Harrington held his first lengthy conversation with Helen Southwell. She had been friendly enough so far, willing to dally for a sentence or two, but too busy to stop.

Now he told her about his conversation with Professor Wainwright.

'Did he say anything interesting?' She seemed in no hurry.

'Several things.'

'Such as?'

'That the eighteenth century is a drawback to those who want promotion in the university hierarchy. The modern period gets you further.'

'Is that the truth?'

'I shouldn't think so. Perhaps some of his acquaintances, Augustan experts, haven't got anywhere. I'd need some statistics.'

'And what else did he say?'

'That this department is so good because he had not appointed extremists.'

'Did you argue?'

'No,' he answered cheerfully. 'He's been very ill, and I doubt whether he could stand up to much bullying.'

'Joe.' She fetched up a small girl's voice. 'Do you think this is a good department?'

'Not bad. But you know that as well as I do. We haven't too many Bradleys. Students seem to want to come here. We aren't as good as Oxford or Cambridge or one or two other places, but they're larger, have more money to flash about.'

'No faults?'

'Dozens. For instance, we need one or two more keen temporary lecturers. But Wainwright's not to blame for that. He'd appoint them if the university would give him the cash. We don't, most of us, moreover, look after the students as well as you do.'

'Clough makes a principle of it. He thinks I spoon-feed them, whereas they'd be better employed finding things out for themselves.'

'Yes, but he doesn't spend the time on them that you do. I guess that the large majority of our students need more help than he's prepared to give. I'll go further. With one or two exceptions our students will learn to learn for themselves better under your guidance than under his lack of it.'

'Flatterer.'

'You know it's true. As you also know I think it's a pity that you spend so much time on them when you could be writing, but I'm prepared to accept your word for it that your own work would not be as good if you could accuse yourself of neglecting your teaching.'

'I haven't finished my book on Spenser, Joe.'

'No, but I don't despair.'

'I do, sometimes. Honestly. I read what I've written, and it seems so obvious or banal that I can't think why I bother.'

'Obvious to you,' Harrington objected, 'because you've spent so much time on it. In my opinion the best sort of criticism is both new and obvious, gives a new slant which, in the end, convinces. I've no time for these clients you can't make head or tail of. A critic of literature is either to be understood, or he's no good.'

'You cheer me, Joe.'

'I hope so. I admire what you do. And for all you say, you seem to know where your length and strength lie. You did right, for instance, not to take up that course on "Feminism and Twentieth Century Literature" that Wainwright was pushing, though you would have made a better job of it than that woman from the history department he roped in.'

'You would have done both, Joe. Spenser and Feminism.'

'Badly. You've the kind of integrity I haven't got. I tackle anything now within reason.'

'Not your "Pre-Romanticism. A Study", Joe. It's a classic.'

'I tried hard then to think properly, as well as to be clever or original or something. But I'd the time. And the pressure on me. It will never happen again.'

Helen drew away with a small sound as if he touched her in some wounded, vital part. Then she looked out of the window, ignoring him, wrapped in self-contemplation. 'It

201

happens with quite a few people.' Harrington continued as if his point needed substantiating. 'You just look how many notables in the profession have done their best work as students for a Ph.D. In subjects like history and literature, we're supposed to grow wiser as we get older, but more often it's not so. We've too many other considerations weighing on us. A pity. I like to think of myself as a prospective sage.'

Harrington suddenly noticed her motionless posture. He grinned, and when she did not move, said,

'Come on, Silas Marner. No time for catalepsy.'

Still she paid no attention.

He rose, walked across, put an arm round her shoulders.

'Cheer up, Helen. It's not a bad world.'

Her flesh responded minimally, to his warm hand. This clever woman needed to be reminded that she belonged to a decent department, that she did well by her students, that she had something to say about literature on her own account. Virtue should be made of sterner stuff.

'I'm a bit of a fool, Joe.'

'By no means.'

She waved her hands at the papers and books about the room.

'This seems an odd way of passing one's life.'

'Yes. More interesting than most.' He neglected her implications.

Helen had not yet moved.

'Are we wasting our lives, Joe?' She spoke in a monotone that sounded machine-made.

'Less than most people. What would we do otherwise? I'd sooner write one good short poem than a good critical book, but would I know if I'd done it? I doubt it, because I'd have the same niggles as I would about a piece of criticism. And it certainly wouldn't earn my living unless I used it to turn myself into a television pundit or an itinerant lecturer in America. And neither would last.'

'Will you show me your poems, Joe, some time?'

'Such as they are.'

'Such as they are.'

Helen turned now, pressed into his chest, kissed his mouth. He pulled her closer. Her green-smeared lids fluttered down. She kissed him again, and again.

'Are you going to write a good poem? Or have you done so already?' Her loins fitted his.

'I don't think so.'

'Why do you say that?' She looked smilingly up.

'I've had the best of my life. That's what I've been trying to tell you.'

'In Cambridge?'

'No. In London.'

'When you were married to Paulina?'

'That was part of it, I must admit. But all the other things. The book. The theatre. The parties. The sense that I was released, at last, that I was making something of my life, that there were exciting things to come, that I was not only doing something but enjoying it.'

'And Paulina broke that up for you?' Helen buried her head into his chest.

'Paulina discovered I was not the man she wanted.'

'Paulina was a bloody fool, then.' A kiss from the now unlifted head.

'By no means. She came to me on the rebound when her judgement was disturbed. I did her a little good for a little while. But she was out of my league. A dull assistant lecturer, about to paddle off to a duller job in the Midlands, wouldn't do for her. Really. She saw it in time. And looked about her for somebody else.'

'Joe, Joe. That's awful.'

'Sensible.'

'But to hurt like that, to wound somebody you had loved, however lightly, is so cruel, selfish.'

'So sensible.'

'Don't keep saying that.'

'I don't want to sound either silly or cynical, but it's near the truth. I didn't understand it at the time any more than I understood how well I was working at Cambridge. I was too battered emotionally to be capable of grasping exactly what was going on. But I had my reward. A well-considered book and at least eighteen months of brilliant life as Paulina's husband.'

'And it will never happen again?' she pressed.

'It's unlikely, but I don't know. Life's too complex for amateur prophecy. I'm getting staid, Helen. I'm like Wainwright tottering around the margins of existence.'

Harrington laughed as he spoke.

'Are you serious?' she asked.

'Never more so.'

She stepped away from him, gently brushing herself down with her fingertips.

'I didn't know I had dandruff.'

'Who watches telly adverts? I could stay here all day, Joe, but I mustn't.'

'Just one more question before you go.' He saw the mixture of alarm and cosy pleasure in her face. 'You've not reconsidered . . . ?' He let the sentence trail away.

'Reconsidered what?' Her mouth tautened, her chin stiff. She knew quite well.

'Marrying me. No, don't say anything just yet. Just let me propose again. Properly, this time.' He stood now perhaps a yard and a half in front of her. 'I love you, Helen. Will you marry me?' Silence crouched. Harrington plunged on. 'I know you suspect it will be the end of the real Helen Southwell, and I suppose there's truth in that. You'll be changed, as I shall. But I want to be changed, and by you, and by nobody else so much. As yet. I can't promise a great deal. We're both set in our ways, though yours are more admirable than mine.' Again, no answer as the tip of her tongue played upon her lips. She crisped her fingers. For a moment he thought she'd stand on her toes, a stiff little robot-instructor. Her breath came and went shallowly. She seemed only half-alive. Once more he began to speak. 'I realize that every sentence I add knocks another crack into an already feeble case, but I love you, Helen.'

'Are you sure?' The question was precise, an examiner's, from a position of superiority.

'Yes.' No need of ornamentation.

'I shall be a comedown after Paulina, Joe. You ought to consider that for my sake as well as your own. Disappointment, seeing you disappointed, I couldn't bear.'

'You don't know how highly I regard you. You'd hold your own with Paulina any day.'

'No. I don't know her, of course, but she cut a brilliant social figure. I'm the wilting flower, or a dying duck.' How broadly her smile spread, then disappeared. 'This needs thinking about.' She spoke as flatly as if she were considering spending an extra pound or two on clothes. 'You know how I feel about you.'

'In that case. . . .'

'In that case nothing of the sort.' She shifted, foot to foot. 'I'm terrified. I nearly married a man at Oxford but withdrew at the last minute. It's not that I'm afraid of spoiling a promising career. You'd probably help me. It's, well, y'know, I'm afraid of losing myself. That doesn't make sense to you. I see you and I see me, separate people. I like what I see of you. Sometimes I think I love it. But why the two of us should hope to live together, or should even consider it, is a mystery. Perhaps I am one of nature's spinsters. I can say all this, Joe, because I've thought it over and over since you proposed at your home. I took it seriously. I know you think I didn't, that I said "No" because you hadn't done it properly. But it's not so. I've been over it time and again. It's not the same thing as Paul's proposal; it's quite different in kind. That shocked me and shook me at first, but I came to terms with it. I knew it would make no sort of marriage that I could share. But with you. I feel it both ways. It could be a success. For me, I mean. Sometimes I want to live with you. The appeal of each belonging to each is strong sometimes. But then, the opposite. . . .' She shrugged her despair.

'Nobody can guarantee anything. We might both change. But now I want to go halves with you, love you for the rest of my life.'

'Should we live together for a trial?' Now the voice was small, wary, bright.

'If that's what you want.' Harrington waved his hands about, drawing meaning from the air. 'I'm old-fashioned. I want to put all my cards down on the table so that you can scrutinize them. You probably regard marriage as a legal contract. Do you? I don't know. I suppose it's sensible. But for me it's far over and above that. The fact that I failed once, just makes me more careful about saying what I'm saying now.'

'But don't you see, Joe, that I might find myself not up to it, and leave you? And then what will happen to you? "Twice", you'll think, "that's twice; there's something wrong with me." '

'I accept that as a possibility, but I'm willing to take the risk.'

She staggered a few inches about the floor, frowning. The dance steps established her distress.

'And what about the effect on Paul?' she asked. 'He's nothing like better yet. If we decided. . . .'

A sharp knock at the door interrupted her. Harrington almost shouted his invitation to enter. A pale, sharp-chinned male face was poked into view.

'Oh, Dr Harrington. Could I ask you about Pope? If you've a minute?'

Harrington stared speechless.

'I can't get hold of the "Letter to Arbuthnot". The library shelves are cleared. Because of the exams.'

'You want just that?'

'I'm going to make it the centre of my argument. If that's sensible?'

'It's always sensible in the exam to have a point of view, provided it gives you an opportunity to splash your learning about.'

Harrington went over to his shelves, took down a school selection of Pope that enthusiastic publishers had sent him for comment.

'You'll find Arbuthnot in there, and a few other useful things, if you must answer on Pope.'

'Do you think I'm unwise to . . . ?'

206

'Why should I say that?'

'You might think I'm not sharp enough for it.'

'Then it's up to you to show me I'm wrong.'

The student waved the book in the air in arabesques of gratitude.

'Thanks for this, Dr Harrington. Dr Southwell.'

He withdrew his peaky face.

'He'll do well to get a third for me,' Helen said.

'Can't make his mind up, and doesn't work hard enough to give himself the chance to form an opinion.'

Helen laughed sadly. Another human failure.

'I, I shall have to get on, Joe.'

'Are you going to marry me? We can't let Weston and his wretched Pope come between us.'

'I can't say "yes", Joe.'

For no reason he began a rambling account of Thomas Reeves and Melanie. Helen drew up a chair to listen, without thought of quitting. Harrington described the afternoon when the pair showed up at his house and demanded to be shown round the garden. 'Now the climax,' he said. 'They've parted. They were only together for a month or two.'

'The difference in age,' Helen murmured in excuse. 'Forty years.'

'Yes. But they tried it.'

'It failed. Hasn't it affected him?'

'I expect so. He says not, but it will have twisted him all right. He wasn't stable to start with. It may even shorten his life.'

'Why do you say that?'

'To add weight,' he came out with it, 'to your view.'

'How did they decide in the first place? What did they say?'

'I don't know. I've tried to imagine it. Perhaps they didn't say anything. Just fell into one another's arms, or bed.'

'Only the likes of us talk?' Helen asked. 'But from what you say they'd hardly known one another, whereas we've been under one another's feet for three years.'

'I'm only just learning, Helen, that I love you.'

'That frightens me. I know about you and Kate Morris-

Jones, people talked, and I expect there were others. Never Helen Southwell. Why not? I shouldn't have said that. You're entitled to your private life. But it terrifies me that you and I, with our different amalgams of experience, should attempt to live together. It wouldn't work.'

'I see.'

'I'm not a virgin.'

'Well,' he said. 'That's that.' He smiled as best he could. 'You may go now.' He tried to infuse humour into the sentence, failed signally, for she began to cry silently, without moving position. Harrington dared not approach her; he demonstrated his inadequacy as a husband by sitting, saying nothing. Finally, grudgingly, against the will of his body he stood, stepped out, touched her. Oddly, she spoke first, relieving him.

'You should marry somebody like that Mrs Selby,' she whispered. 'She'd be normal, and sexy and efficient. And I was convinced she loved you.'

'She'd have to dump a husband and two youngish sons. She wouldn't do that easily.'

'I said somebody like her. Not her, particularly.'

'Oh, Helen.'

'Somebody will interrupt us again,' she said, looking up at him. 'To borrow an epithalamion.' She had made a joke. ' "My love is now awake out of her dreams." '

Helen stood, gently releasing herself from the hand on her shoulder, before leaning over her desk to pick up the half dozen books she had abandoned earlier.

'I'll be off,' she said. 'I'll think about this, if I may.'

'I don't know,' he answered thickly, 'if we're serious. We seem to be floating a yard or two up in the air above the subject.'

'Do you mean you are, or I am?'

'I won't answer that and make things worse.'

She looked smart now, taut, her face dry, her books held at the ready, sharp enough to take the world on.

'I'm sorry, Joe. I'm hopeless. Will you ask me again when I've finished my Spenser?'

'This isn't a bloody game, you know. Just look at. . . .'

'No,' she said. 'Don't argue. I meant that, but . . . I think I know what arguments you're about to put. But I meant it. I was serious, and I'm sorry.'

Helen left the room.

Now he was weighted down; he had opened his heart and the chosen one could not respond, nor could he convince her. Disappointment cramped him, physical weakness. She seemed the stronger of the two, able to repulse him, to search about in her head for the small jokes, the quotations. Just as she felt unable to complete her study of Spenser, deliberately refusing to write down the obvious or second-hand, so now she set her face against marriage because what she could offer was lukewarm, the thin gruel of affection. Harrington gripped the edge of his desk, angry now with himself, not knowing where to turn next. His eyes ran along his bookshelves, reading nothing; literature displayed no salve.

Forcing himself, he took down Spenser, opening the book at 'Epithalamion', making no sense of the words, turning barren pages.

> But if ye saw that which no eyes can see
> The inward beauty of her lively spright,
> Garnished with heavenly gifts of high degree.

He closed the book, returned it to the shelves, old-maidishly straightening the volumes so that Helen would not know he'd read there, had searched and failed. He straightened his chair at his desk, put on his summer mackintosh, made his way downstairs. The place echoed to his footsteps, empty and hollow. He tried with bravado to whistle Bach's 'My heart ever faithful, Sing praises, be joyful', and failed. He blew breath over his lips, wasting the effort.

Outside it seemed warmer than indoors, but lacked sunshine.

Harrington pushed himself hard, to expel his disappointment. Again he failed, finding that unless he concentrated on movement his feet dragged, shuffled in short steps, motion

209

petering out until he loitered, staring about him vaguely in search of bearings, a spiritless copy of himself. Now he was like Reeves, left to his own resources. The old man had been prepared, starving in a Japanese work camp, so that nothing subsequently would break his spirit. Harrington swore at a silver birch.

He remembered Paulina's announcement that their marriage was at an end.

'I'm sorry to have to say this, Joe. . . .' she had begun. She had lunched out with two women friends and had been drinking, but informed him clearly that in her view their marriage had come to nothing. Only the repetition of this, in the same pointed words, suggested alcohol.

'Is there someone else?' he had asked, expecting a negative answer.

'Yes, there is. But there wouldn't have been if things had been right between us.'

'Who is he?'

'Edmond Benson.'

The name meant nothing; he had not heard of the man. Paulina had immediately put herself to bed for the afternoon, while he had sat in his chair, suffering, trying to understand the nature and extent of his pain. He wept, discovered himself groaning. Her announcement had smashed him in surprise. Now and then in the last six months she had said with a cheerful tolerance, 'I don't know why we married. It won't last', but he had not believed her. Today's casual statement, with its damning rider, so precisely delivered from a cloud of gin and perfume had cut him to size. That afternoon, too, he had walked the streets, passing bright plate glass, market stalls, middle-aged women out shopping, cats and dogs reflected in windows and shadowed on pavements, with his face frozen, his body reduced so that his suit bagged on him, two sizes too large. When he returned Paulina was still in bed. Cravenly he kept out of her way.

In the following weeks they quarrelled, shouting each other down, hissing insults, with no recourse to civility or reason. They had fought physically and once he, surprised by her strength, had punched her with ferocity on the cheekbone, knocking her back over a chair, stinging his knuckles. 'Get up,' he had shouted, but she had wriggled into the seat and hunched there, face down, refusing to move, silent as the grave. When he saw her next her face was ugly with bruises, and he had felt both ashamed and sickly triumphant. She had moved out, efficiently, without notice, a week later just when he was beginning to consider lodgings elsewhere. In the middle of his distress he had been interviewed and accepted for his present position. He could just remember, and was grateful for, the questions the panel flung at him, catching his interest, temporarily cracking the carapace of his loneliness. The world creaked chaotically past him, a mixture of trivial duties or chores with a punishing incoherence of emotional strain.

He had recovered, but only after a fashion.

It had taken time; he had behaved more generously towards Paulina than his solicitor thought proper. He had bought, after protracted negotiation, the family house from his sister, and set about furnishing it. This and the preparation of new courses had muddled him through, but his wounds stung raw yet. An explosion of private anger, of longing, a heightened sense of Paulina's physical presence could split and scar his leisure time. These appeared more infrequently, but he could imagine their smart burning into him in old age.

This afternoon, in the park, in early summer, he stood and stared into a shrubbery, rejected again. Unhappy at Cambridge, he had fought his desperate corner and had won; rescued by Paulina he had been flattened again. Now, once more ye laurels; Helen had spurned him. The darkness between the trees, on the bushes, seemed beautiful, the earth's best, damp and nasty.

Harrington walked on. A professor from the chemistry department, doctor of science, F.R.S., nodded affably, saying summer had come at last, not before time. Momentarily pleased, Harrington quickened his step, but soon dawdled again, among tall trees. Helen had pushed him aside as she had Wainwright, though she claimed there were differences, as she had the fiancé at Oxford. He blamed himself because he had not proposed when she needed him, would have accepted him. There was no telling whether this surmise was correct; for all he knew once a man came out into the open with his offer she closed herself. He could not understand her; one moment she dissolved into tears, the next she joked, made a neat quotation, scored an academic point, looked spry. The variety was not infinite, no, but too complex for his comfort. He set his teeth; he would bear all, shout and bawl back at the bleak world like Thomas Reeves.

He reached a litter bin made of sawn logs, stopped, and standing there, emptied the pockets of his mac: screwed bits of paper, receipts, fluff. Somebody had thrown into the metal receptacle at the centre the carton from an electric iron, here, with milk bottle tops, in rusticity, two hundred and fifty yards from the nearest building. He would not forget this place.

Four days later, on Sunday morning, he recalled the pause by the waste paper bin when Tony Selby telephoned that his father-in-law, Tom Reeves, had attempted to hang himself in an outhouse, kicking a backless chair from under him. He had been alive when a neighbour, round with a few bedding plants, had cut him down, but had died on Saturday night, in hospital, where his weak heart had given out.

Harrington mouthed conventional sympathy, and this seemed acceptable.

'How's Anne taking it?' he asked.

'She's shocked, as you can imagine, but she'll come to terms with it. She'd made her mind up to go round that afternoon.'

'Did he leave a note?'

'Apparently not. We haven't found one.'

Reeves, the writer, had satisfied himself with chair and clothesline. With them he had failed, equally.

Harrington's symbol of obduracy had cracked and this did not altogether surprise him.

'Does the Critchlow woman know?'

'I've left a message. At her office.'

When Harrington told Helen on Monday, she opened her mouth, guiltily, unable to speak. Perhaps she had remembered that he had said the break-up would shorten Reeves's life.

'It's awful,' she whispered, in the end. Dumbed by his obvious misery.

He turned to his books; he could just about read now.

'And the daughter?' she asked. 'Anne?'

'Managing,' her husband said. She has her boys to think of, her home.'

'Oh, Joe. It's dreadful.' Language deserted her tongue.

He did not answer. In the end, not quickly, holy Helen opened the door, went out, softly closed it. He had not looked round; she had been groping, choking for words. Later that afternoon he found a note from her on his desk. It did not mention marriage, but asked him to convey sympathy to Anne. 'Tell her that anything I can do, I will.' He put it into the clean pocket of his mackintosh. He'd carry the message. The air in the room seemed arctic.

Today, Wednesday, by the litter basket he wiped the dust from his hands. He had blackened, thinly, the nail of his middle finger.

Harrington set his face, made for his room, towards the work he could not start at present. Helen had no conception, he thought, of what she had done.

His steps, brisk up to a dozen, faltered.